MARJORY FLEMING

Marjory Fleming

From a water-colour drawing by Isabella Keith

MARJORY FLEMING

by

ORIEL MALET

FABER AND FABER LIMITED
24 Russell Square
London

First published in Mcmxlvi
by Faber and Faber Limited
24 Russell Square London W.C.1
Printed in Great Britain by
Western Printing Services Limited Bristol

Note

This is the story of a child. Much of it is any child—that was Marjory's charm. For the rest I have tried to show her as I think she was, and not as I should have liked her to be. I have drawn all the facts in this book from Marjory's own Journals, and her own and contemporary letters. I have been much helped by Mr. L. McBean's charming book *The Story of Pet Marjorie* and it is from this book that I have dated the three Journals. Other books from which I have obtained information have been: *Pet Marjorie*, by Dr. John Brown; *The Journals, Letters, and Verses of Marjory Fleming*, in facsimile, edited by Arundell Esdail; and *The Complete Marjory Fleming*, edited by Frank Sidgwick.

I have purposely omitted any reference to Walter Scott and Marjory Fleming, because on investigation I have not found sufficient evidence to bear out the legend that has grown up about this, although they were distantly related. Dr. John Brown's *Pet Marjorie* appears to have given rise to this theory, although it was in fact a work of fiction, based on a letter from Mrs. Elizabeth Fleming, in which she mentioned the friendship between Scott and Miss Keith. Probably he saw Marjory when he went to tea there; certainly she is never mentioned in his letters, nor he in Marjory's Journals, except as the author of her favourite poem *Helvellyn*. Therefore, since this book is chiefly concerned with the people and events that were important and dear to Marjory, I have left him out of it.

I should like to thank the Rev. Andrew T. Richardson for the kind help he has given me, and for allowing me to reproduce a picture of Marjory in the front of this book. I am also very sincerely grateful to Miss A. B. Luke, Librarian, for her kindness and assistance to me when I visited Kirkcaldy.

Contents

You can give them your love, but not your thoughts
For they have their own thoughts.
You can house their bodies, but not their souls,
For their souls dwell in the house of to-morrow.
You can strive to be like them,
But seek not to make them like you.
For life goes not backward, nor tarries with yesterday.

THIRD CENTURY PERSIAN POET,
WRITING OF CHILDREN

Illustrations

To
YVONNE ARNAUD
with
love and gratitude

PART I

Kirkcaldy: 1806

All day it had rained, mistily, steadily, with a sound of sighing among the leaves. Now, at evening, it ceased. A pale gleam of sky showed in the west; the sun disappeared in a burst of sudden crimson, splashing the grey slate roofs with colour. The town looked ready to tumble into the sea. A light wind sprang up. It blew inland, racing up the main street of Kirkcaldy, and flung the dripping sprays of creepers against the windows by a house at the furthest end, between the country and the sea.

There was a child in the garden. She stood at the end of the path. It was cold, and she had wrapped her hands in her white dress. She stood with her feet planted firmly apart, her short hair blown by the wind, her mouth open, gulping fresh air. It was lovely, after being shut up in the house all day. The clouds swept by, a thousand miles above; under her feet, the long grasses streamed out, shining with rain. Something fierce, unchildlike, stirred within her. She wanted to shout aloud into the wind, but was silent. Her spirit, tugging, seemed ready to burst from the three-year-old body that held it. For a moment she seemed ageless, apart.

'Marjory!'

A quiver passed across her face, and was gone. She set her shoulders more squarely to the wind. From her lips, unconsciously clenched, came a thin thread of sound as she began to hum, carelessly, to show how little she minded. They had sent Isabella to find her. Silly Isy, who was afraid of the dark, of the wind, of the strange branches tapping against the window pane at night. Marjory was part of these things. What she dreaded, what she hated, so that she stiffened with the force of her

13

horror, was the sound of quarrelling, of singing from the street outside. It meant people, safety, to Isabella. Marjory, agonized, could not sleep for an hour afterwards. She never told anyone.

Through the gathering darkness, lights sprang up in the house behind her. Isabella's questing steps came nearer. A flash of white between the bushes guided her. She stepped carefully because it had been raining. Gleaming puddles lay on the paths. Stay-at-home Isabella saw nothing marvellous in the sopping, windswept garden, but they would scold if she did not fetch her sister in, and she liked peace.

'Marjory!' she called again, impatiently, for the small white figure at the end of the path had not moved an inch.

The glory faded. Wind, cloud, sky, took on their natural forms again. She was no more a part of them, their mystery pulling her out of the world she knew. She was suddenly a cross, tired child in a white frock which was wet and muddy in patches where she had wiped her fingers on it. No more than that.

'Bad Isy!' she said, decidedly, something telling her that it had gone because they had called her. She would have come by herself in a minute.

'Bad Maidie, to run out like that in the rain,' returned Isabella, who was three years older, a demure child in a high-waisted frock, with a mild expression. She used, instinctively, a tone she had caught from their mother. You could see her grown-up, with children, all in that instant. Some destinies are easy to trace, Isabella, at six, was already everything she would become.

'Come,' she coaxed, taking her sister's hand.

Marjory pulled free. Escaping, she ran behind a bush. Brushing past it, she sent a shower of little drops down on her upturned face, and laughed aloud. Isabella, alone on the path, between the puddles and the swift darkness, was suddenly overcome.

'Oh, *Maidie*,' she wailed, with a hint of tears in her voice.

There was silence. Marjory stood quite still. The leaves

14

danced up and down, but she no longer laughed. Could Isy *really* be going to cry? Why? It was *lovely* outside, when it was nearly dark. She ran anxiously back on to the path.

'I'll be good! I'll be good!' she promised, standing on her toes to look into Isabella's face. Taking hands again, they began to go up the path towards the house, and bed.

The house the Flemings lived in was on the High Street, and it was interesting because the ground floor was a shop. It was owned by a book-seller, and Marjory called him Mr. Parcel. That alone was something to treasure. Looking down from the rooms above, she often watched him setting his books out in the window, or coming out to see a customer down the street. She wondered if he wrapped himself in brown paper when he went to bed, but when she asked Jeanie Robertson, their nurse, she was shocked. Before Marjory was two years old, instinct told her that grown people were very often shocked.

Another very good thing about living over Mr. Parcel's shop, was that you had only to go downstairs when you wanted a book. Mr. Fleming was always doing this, and he had a room of his own that was very like the shop, except that the books in it were not for sale. All the Flemings liked books, and it made Jeanie Robertson extremely cross because she had to dust them. Marjory was her favourite, and William, who was eight, and a great tease, said it was because she could not yet read. When he said this, she bent her head low, low, so that they should not see her burning cheeks. She wanted so much to read, at almost four years old, but the letters refused to make words, so what could she do? Instead, she listened to her father. Mr. Fleming, with his wife and two children, William and Isabella, had come to Kirkcaldy soon after his brother had been appointed minister there. Marjory was born in the house above the shop. Her father had settled in the town as an accountant, and worked for various big shipping and industrial firms. They were quite well off. Mrs. Fleming, who had been Isabella Rae before her marriage, was the daughter of an eminent Edinburgh surgeon. Her sister had married the younger son of Keith of Ravelston, and was wealthy, with a big house in Edinburgh, and Ravelston to visit when she liked. It seemed quite grand to the Fleming children, and they liked to hear their mother speak of their rich Edinburgh cousins, whom Marjory had never yet seen, and the others but seldom. Mr. Fleming was prouder of his own family, who were of Highland descent, and he told his children wonderful tales of their grandfather, who had fought for Prince Charlie at Culloden. Especially he told these tales when William was home from school. It was as if he wanted to make the boy proud of his heritage, those shadowy people with the same blood, the same features, binding William, Isabella, even little Marjory to the past. Marjory at three years old, was not supposed to be interested in such tales, but she sat with her mouth wide open, propped against the footstool, listening. No-one knew what she thought. Sometimes, in the flickering light, it seemed as if it was her father himself who had fought in that distant battle long ago. When Marjory thought like this, her mouth opened even wider. She pushed against the stool so hard in her excitement that she tumbled to the floor in a heap of white muslin and red shoes; was noticed, whisked up, and carried to bed.

The entrance to the house from the street was through an arched doorway. The kitchen was on the ground floor, at the back of the shop. Coming in from the garden it was now nearly dark, but seen through the archway, the street seemed lighter. It was like the edge of another world. Mr. Parcel had put up his shutters and gone home. Marjory kept close, close to her sister, away from the street with its sinister dark puddles and its wet cobblestones winking like a hundred evil little eyes. She was *afraid* of the street, and though she did not utter a word, heaved a deep sigh when Isabella opened the door and they tumbled into the narrow hall, and saw the kitchen fire blazing cheerily through the half-open door.

Mrs. Fleming, back from paying a call, was standing beside the fire talking to Jeanie Robertson. Marjory flew ahead of Isabella to get the first kiss. She buried herself almost completely in the folds of the thick cloak, lined with scarlet, which her mother wore in bad weather. Marjory liked it, 'because it

16

smells of journeys' she said, for, never having been on a journey, she liked the sound of one.

'There's my precious lamb, coming like a good girl at her bedtime!' exclaimed Jeanie, holding up her hands in amazement, for everything Marjory did was wonderful to her.

Marjory, turning from her, buried herself more securely in the cloak. She knew that Jeanie admired her, and because her own affections remained untouched, she took it for granted, bullying, coaxing, never giving her a moment's peace. Mrs. Fleming knew it too, and was troubled, she watched her children anxiously, as they developed, and traced in Marjory a wayward streak. If it went on, the child would become insupportable at the expense of her older sister.

'It was wrong to run out in the garden, and leave poor Isabella to find you, now was it not, Maidie?' she asked gently, smiling at Isabella, who stood a little apart, watching. She lifted her head and smiled back, gratefully. Mrs. Fleming had sense and tact. Her soft voice drew Isabella into the circle, lifted the focus from laughing Marjory, who was tugging unrepentant at the strings of the cloak. Before she could do any more, Jeanie Robertson broke in:

'Ay, and wrong of her sister, ma'am, to leave the poor wee lamb on her own so long. If Isabella was more careful, it would never have happened. I am sure of it. The child got tired of playing all alone, didn't you, then, Maidie?'

'No,' said Marjory, playing with the strings of the cloak.

'It's time she was in bed, at any rate,' said Mrs. Fleming hastily. 'Run off with Jeanie, Maidie, and remember not to run out when it has rained, again. You might catch a cold through doing so.'

'Where's William?' demanded Marjory, undeterred. 'I want him to take me upstairs on his back.' She paused. 'He's with Papa, I think.'

'You can run in to your father, and ask William if he will play,' said Mrs. Fleming, as she went up the stairs to her room. 'But mind, if he is busy you're not to tease.'

William *was* busy, kneeling at a corner of the big desk, with

B   17

a great many pieces of paper and coloured pencils scattered
round him, the candles from under a pink silk shade, flushed
his cheeks. He was drawing a map of Scotland, and afterwards
colouring it blue, red, green. Marjory impressed with everything William did, liked this too. Slipping from her father's
knee, she came to stand at his elbow, perfectly silent, her lips
pressed together with the effort of keeping so still.

'Where's Kirkcaldy?' she asked at last, in a whisper.

'Yonder,' said William, jerking his pencil, but before she
could find it he added, 'Don't touch it, child, or you'll make a
smudge.'

Marjory drew back her finger and put both her hands behind
her back, out of harm's way. There was silence. Presently she
tugged at his sleeve.

'Take me upstairs!' she said, coaxing. He flung down his
pencil and frowned tremendously. 'You're a nuisance!' he said,
gathering up the precious crayons in case even one should be
lost. She knew he did not mean it, and stood waiting. In the
candlelight, her great dark eyes, fearless, gazed away over his
head into the corners of the room. For a moment, she seemed
once more to lose touch of time, as she had done in the garden.
Then she burst out laughing, and tossed back her head so gladly
that her father started and laid down his newspaper to watch
her carried triumphantly out of the room and up the stairs
amid shrieks of delight.

She was not a small child for her age, and heavy; William
staggered a little as he mounted the stairs and trudged down
the passage.

'You're a fine weight,' he exclaimed, as he tipped her into
Jeanie Robertson's arms at the end of the journey.

'The finest wee lass in Scotland!' declared the old woman,
tossing her up and down, which Marjory did not like so much.
At evening, Jeanie wore her best brooch of big blue stones that
scratched if you did not take care. She wriggled free as soon as
she could. The love she took for granted; it had lapped her
round since the day of her birth. Sometimes, when excited or
glad, she flew unbidden to kiss her father. Morning and evening

18

Mrs. Fleming kissed her. The child, submitting, remained curiously untouched. She supposed she loved her family, because everyone did; if you did not, you were wicked. Marjory was anxious not to be wicked. She listened to Jeanie's stories on Sunday, and the devil sprang up from the depths of the kitchen fire, to mock her. Hell seemed a very real place, as she listened; then, almost as easily, forgot.

While Jeanie pulled off the crumpled white dress and prepared the bath, she sat on the edge of the bed kicking her toes up and down and singing a song she had made up herself on the spur of the moment. She just let the words flow through her head, and they came out through her lips like that. The meaning was not important. It lasted all the time she was actually being washed, drinking her milk, and in some strange way it mingled with her prayers. When this happened her mother, standing by the bed in a dove-grey taffeta gown that rustled, shook her head.

'*Think* what you're saying, Maidie,' she implored. But if God knew everything, he *must* know what she meant. Marjory, her hands neatly folded tip to tip, suddenly shouted out 'Amen!' as loudly as possible, and lay down flat. Mrs. Fleming sighed.

Now, in the light from the candle beside the bed, the child's face took on the solemnity of evening. In that brief instant, she recaptured something of the exaltation she had felt in the garden, but quietened now with dreams. The mother, leaning over for the evening kiss, felt she no longer knew her child. Then, in a flash, Maidie's arms were around her, clinging to her, asking the night-time question of every child:

'Don't go! Where will you be?'

'Only downstairs, reading to Isabella. I'll leave the door open, so you can see.'

Marjory lay down again quietened. She watched her mother blow out the candle, leave the room. A thin slit of light showed through the door, like a finger pointing. She felt wide awake now, and sat up, eager to see at what it was pointing. A book, left open on the table. Marjory climbed out of bed and tiptoed across the room to look closer. There were no pictures, and confronted with the black and white symmetry of the print, which was small and close, and peppered with long curly S's, she felt a definite sense of frustration. Why couldn't she read, when she wanted to so much?

She flicked over the pages in desperation. The light fell on the title page. There, in big black letters, was a whole row of words. Looking at them, Marjory suddenly found they said 'The Mouse, and Other Tales', and were no longer just a jumble of letters. Even while she stood a little bewildered, in front of her own small miracle, a door slammed somewhere downstairs, and voices floated up from below. Closing the book, she scampered back to bed, and almost at once fell fast asleep.

The beam of light continued to point at the book, as though it held a purpose for the life that lay sleeping within the room.

Next day, when she awoke, the first thing that Marjory remembered was that she could read. She had made out 'The Mouse, and Other Tales' all by herself. For a moment she lay breathless before this discovery. She would not have to wait any more until people had time to read to her; Isabella stumbled sometimes over quite easy words, even at six years old, and Jeanie Robertson pitched her voice on a peculiar high note when she read aloud. It was not very easy to follow when they did things like that. If she could read to herself, it would be a different thing. She could chose anything she liked, then. It would not be 'Oh, Maidie—we had that yesterday. Find something else!' any more.

Far down the street a clock struck seven. It was repeated by all the clocks down the road until it reached their own grandfather clock in the passage, whose inside was full of weights and chains, which made Marjory rather uneasy when the little door was left open after dusting. To-day she felt, something quite special was going to happen to her. To begin with, it was not raining like yesterday. When the curtains swung gently out into the room, the sunshine fell on the boards like water, and she could hear the faint rustle of the leaves. She glanced across at Isabella lying asleep at the other side of the room, with her hair plaited into two little stumps tied with red ribbons. She looked like a doll. Isabella never lay awake and wondered about anything. Every day she woke up at exactly the right time, opened her eyes immediately, and was patient, good-tempered, and quiet. She never had moods. It would have been more fun if she did; she might have been awake at that moment, talking to Marjory and listening while she read aloud *The Mouse, and Other Tales*, instead of lying fast asleep, while only her shadow danced in the uncertain sun.

Marjory looked round the room; she had seen everything in it, exactly the same, last night, but now it seemed different, quickened with morning. The night-light had burned itself out into a mass of tallow. Sometimes, the splodges formed themselves into curious shapes, a cat, a flower, a little man. No-one could see them but Marjory, and even she had to be quick because Jeanie called it 'messing', and whisked the saucer away at once. On the table, as well as the night-light was a Bible, and lying beside it (because Jeanie said to lay anything on top of the Holy Book was a sin) she could see *The Mouse, and Other Tales*. She scrambled out of bed backwards, because it was rather high, landing with a thump on the mat that made the soap-dish on the washing-stand clink, and would have wakened anyone but Isabella. For a while she stood anxiously on one foot, waiting to see if it had or not, then she ran across to the table and lifting down the book, she carried it over to the window, where she could see. Her hand trembled with eagerness as she turned the page. No-one knew how much she wanted to read! Part of it came from her innate sense of independence; she *hated* the way people read to her, and always at the wrong times. Her father was an exception, but he was often busy and his readings were kept as a treat or a reward. Besides, most people read what they thought suitable. Marjory wanted more. Perhaps she did not consciously know this; impossible that she should. It was not on the surface of her mind, the little-girl part of her; it was hidden farther, deeper, in the part that responded to the rain and wind, and the feel of the sun. The things that made her Marjory Fleming, a person, and not just a child of three in her nightgown, holding a book.

21

'Once upon a time,' she whispered in a gulp, and found the whole page was made plain to her. She *could* read. On and on she went, down the page, and her voice came louder and clearer, until she was shouting it out in a song of triumph, and thumping her toes on the floor. It certainly woke Isabella and that was something. She sat up in bed wide-eyed, and stared. Jeanie Robertson, coming in with a jug of hot water, set it down on the floor and held up her hands.

'Playing! In front of the window too,' she exclaimed. 'You'll catch your death, child.'

Marjory looked round. The shadow of her hair fell straight and brown across her cheek. She held the book firmly in her two hands. Suddenly, coldly she said:

'I'm *reading*, not playing. Can't you see the difference?'

It was her rudest voice. Isabella would most certainly have been rebuked for using it. Jeanie picked up the jug and poured the water into a blue china basin. She did not say anything at all. Isabella had gone to sleep again.

'I'm reading!' said Marjory, looking quickly round at her audience. Jeanie went on pouring and splashing, clattering the soap dish. Now she was dipping her little finger in the water to see if it was too hot. Isabella still slept, her shoulder turned to the room. Marjory stared at them.

'Look! Watch me,' she commanded. Then, pulling the book off the table, she went to the door.

'I'm going to read to Mama!' she said, and marched out of the room with her head in the air. Her shadow danced down the passage in front of her. She pushed open the door of her parent's bedroom, and stood for a moment just inside, wrinkling her toes on the unfamiliar carpet. Then she climbed up on the bed with the book tucked under her arm.

'Good morning, Mud. I've come to read to you,' she said, using the baby name she had made for her mother when she was too small to say anything else. Mrs. Fleming looked at her daughter considering her, and sighed. She did not know what to make of her sometimes.

'You ought to be with Jeanie, getting dressed, Marjory,' she said. 'Why can you not do the right thing at the right time, like Isabella?'

The door into the dressing-room opened. She looked up at once. Her father stood there all ready to go down to his breakfast. Marjory heaved a contented sigh; between them there flashed a look of understanding. She tipped back her head with a radiant smile as he came towards the bed.

'Let Marjory show us what she can do, my love,' he said. 'Read away, Maidie. We're listening.'

Delighted, she started off at once in her clear, light voice, without a stumble. Only, towards the end of the page the words came quicker and quicker, in gulps. When at last she slammed the book shut her cheeks were quite pink. Her father caught her up and tossed her into the air. 'Well done, Maidie,' he said approvingly. 'That's the way to go on. I'll swear you can read anything now. We won't have you long at the Mouse's Tale. You can tumble yourself into the library, and see what you find there to please you.'

'Nonsense, James, you'll make a perfect fool of that child!' said Mrs. Fleming, half laughing. 'Marjory must keep to what she can understand. She's not four yet.'

'But I can read,' insisted Marjory, nodding her head very wisely from the top of the bed.

'Yes, I wish you were half so quick to obey your Mamma and Jeanie! There, I can hear her calling you.'

The child slid at once from the bed and would have run after her father, but he shut the door before she caught up with him, and the handle was too high for her to reach. She turned disconsolately away, and picked up the book.

'Maidie.'

She stopped, and came near the bed. Mrs. Fleming leaned over and stroked her hair, gently, pushing it away from her eyes.

'I'm pleased you can read, Maidie,' she said, softly. 'Don't think I am not. Only you must try as hard to be good and obedient, and not cross to your sister. Then I shall be proud of you too. There! Now you must run to Jeanie, and be dressed.'

23

'Yes,' said Maidie inscrutably, rubbing the quilt against her cheek. To turn the subject, she asked:

'Can I wear the white dress with the blue ribbons to-day? I'll take care not to soil it.'

'Yes, if you wish. But you must not carry the cats if you do, or they'll tear the embroidery.'

Marjory's face fell. She ran from the room as eagerly as she had come, in case they should tell her not to do anything else. Outside the door, her spirits rose again. She had read to her father, and he was glad, as she had known he would be. Mud did not care so much; she only thought about manners. Now she could read any book; her father had said so. Tossing her head, she ran back into the nursery, calling out:

'Quick, Jeanie! Dress me! I can wear my white dress to-day because I can read.'

Isabella was standing on the footstool, having her curls brushed in, as she did every day. It took a great time, because Jeanie twisted each one round her finger. When they were done, she tied them up with a blue ribbon. They hung neatly and prettily to Isabella's shoulders; her hair had just the faintest curl in it, and always looked tidy. Marjory's hair was as straight as could be, and even cut short as it was, it fell into her eyes. No ribbon could stay in it for more than a minute, with the way she shook and tossed her head in the sun, like a little wild pony set free. She was proud of her white dress with the blue sash, which was kept for special occasions. Jeanie pressed her to put on a pinafore over it, but Maidie stamped her foot and looked so cross, she declared she felt quite frightened and put it back in the cupboard. Marjory laughed, but she went downstairs without a pinafore.

It is all very well to be dressed in your best for an hour or two, but before the morning was over she began to feel it rather a trial. She saw William off to school, and waved to him from under the archway, then returned rather sadly to the house. The cat was sitting on the window sill, fast asleep. Marjory stopped to contemplate it, on her way indoors. The cat had very long whiskers. She counted them longingly with her hands behind her back, but she could not pick him up and hug him as she usually did, because she was wearing her white dress. She sighed. Isabella Heron, a child of her own age who lived next door, came out into the garden with a cupful of earth and water to make mud pies, and turn them out on a flat stone. She invited Marjory to join her.

'I'm wearing my best dress,' Marjory admitted, rather self-consciously, casting a longing look at the cup. Isabella looked surprised.

'It's no' your birthday, is it?' she inquired with interest. Marjory shook her head.

'Then what are you wearing it for?'

She looked round a little desperately, then burst out:

'I wanted to!'

'How silly!' said Isabella scornfully. She was never allowed to wear *her* best dress, which was a rather hideous tartan silk, except at Christmas or her birthday. Just at the moment it made her feel superior.

'You can't play with mud then, I suppose,' she went on. 'That's a pity, because it's *just* right to-day. I expect it's the rain. I'm going to make a plum cake.'

Marjory watched her listlessly. Suddenly it made her cross to see Isabella mixing the earth and water with such gusto, and murmuring happily to herself. She decided not to stay and watch. Isabella was still at her lessons. Marjory climbed the stairs to the nursery, where she flung herself down on her own small chair next to Jeanie Robertson, and put her chin in her hands.

'Oh dear me! There's *nothing* to do!' she sighed, but she wouldn't say why.

Jeanie Robertson gave her a swift, sharp look over the top of her spectacles. Then she pushed them up on to her fore-head and looked at Marjory again. After a minute she said rather sourly, 'Well, after ye've had your dinner, I'll take ye and Isabella for a walk in Raith grounds. How will that be?'

That cleared the air at once. Marjory's face shone, and she

was quite glad after all to be dressed in her best. Raith estate lay just a mile from Kirkcaldy, near enough for the children to spend many summer days picnicking there, but too far for them to go by themselves. The waterfall enchanted Marjory especially, for she had a child's love of playing in even the smallest puddle. It was not always that Jeanie could be persuaded to take them, certainly not if she had her rheumatics come on bad, which they always seemed to do at quite the wrong time. The day, that until then had fallen decidedly flat, soared once more to the heights it had attained that morning. Marjory's happiness flew to her head at once, as it always did. The whole house was not big enough to contain her excitement. Upstairs she ran and then downstairs, looking for Isabella. She found her sitting at her lessons in the parlour, quiet and placid. When she heard they were to spend the afternoon at Raith, she did not fling down her books, or jump up in excitement, or do any of the things she had hoped she would do. She just said 'Very well,' and returned to her book. Marjory was disappointed. As she had nothing particular to do, she stayed where she was, and built up a pile of slate pencils on the polished table. They fell over with a crash, and rolled on to the floor. Isabella said 'Don't, Maidie', without looking up. Marjory came and leaned against her. She tried to see over her sister's shoulder, but could not quite manage it.

Soon after dinner they set out, walking primly one each side of Jeanie Robertson. They were not allowed to break free from her until they left the high street. Marjory paused on tip-toe to peep into Mr. Parcel's shop as they turned out of the archway; all last week there had been a book in the window lying open at the most fascinating page. There was a picture of a lady floating down a river in a sea-green dress, scattered with flowers; underneath on a scroll, was written 'Ophelia'. Marjory thought this a strange and lovely name; she wished it was her own. Miss Ophelia Fleming would sound extremely well, she thought. As a result, the picture fascinated her and she was even ready to brave the horrors of the street to look at it. Unfortunately, she had to stand on her toes to see it, and Jeanie was not always willing to wait. This afternoon she pulled Marjory away before she had time to see anything.

'We can't stand all the day gawping into shop windows,' was all the explanation she would give, as she tugged the child away, and hurried her down the street.

They entered Raith through the smallest lodge gate, which generally stood open. Marjory had never seen anyone open the big scrolled-iron centre gate, and by now she had ceased to believe that it opened at all. As usual, she was straining forward with excitement before they had even turned the corner. She had a most passionate love of nature, but at three years old it was purely instinctive. Something in the woods and lakes drew her out of herself, made her what she had been that stormy evening in the garden; she stood still in the centre of the path, her eyes opened wide to all the beauty she saw around her. The great golden beech-trees fell down to the water's edge and, restlessly unreal, their reflections rose to meet them, until water and earth became nothing but brown and gold, screening the blue October sky. Jeanie's footsteps on the lake path were muffled by fallen leaves; they dropped silently down on the water, and caught in the children's hair. Isabella walked along as quietly as she had done in the High Street; she kept beside Jeanie, whose watchful eye, as always, was on Marjory. She, wild with sudden liberty, was never still for an instant; she darted ahead up the path or lingered behind to stare entranced when, with a sudden whirr of wings that made her heart thump, a duck flew out across the water. Marjory was still at the somewhat unfortunate age when everything was several sizes too large for her. The lake stretched out, an immense sea, to her right. A small crimson bush rose like a tower of flame in front of her. Only the very lowest branches were hers to pick unaided, and as she liked to touch everything that pleased her, and was yet fiercely independent, she contented herself with plucking up leaves from the path. Soon she had a fistful of yellow and brown ones, and was quite happy. She felt that Raith and the whole world (which just now were the same things) belonged to her. Filled with a new sense of importance

she ran ahead up the path, leaving Isabella and Jeanie to come
sedately in her wake, talking as usual of quite dull things.
Isabella never ran and played, even with other children.

'Not too far, Maidie,' she heard behind her, breaking into
her delight. 'We're turning back at the corner.'

Marjory stopped. Her whole face clouded; her body stiffened
and became unyielding as a rock; her two hands clutched the
leaves firmly and would not let go. She looked as obstinate and
sour as she could. Isabella, knowing the signs, sighed. Jeanie,
who could be quite as obstinate herself, rumbled on unheeding.
'It's too far for ye to walk to the waterfall just now. We'll go
up to the mill-race and come back again.'

Marjory looked up the path. At the end of it there was a
sluice running under a wooden bridge. She sometimes stood
there, with her mother holding her firmly by the skirts, to
throw sticks into the water. She hardly ever went further, except on a rare treat with her father. Over the wooden bridge
the path turned a corner and branched into two. You could
either climb up to the waterfall, or go tamely back round the
other side of the lake. Marjory liked water and she felt rebellious. She wanted to see the cataract come crashing down between the rocks like thunder. It frightened her, but the fear
held such fascination, she wanted to feel it again. It was not
evil, like the unknown fear of the street at night.

'I want to go,' she said, frowning. She kicked the leaves with
her feet.

'Then want must be your master,' snapped Jeanie, annoy-
ingly, and made a big mistake. If she had simply turned and
begun walking back, Marjory would have followed, and forgotten her grievance on the way. She would never have stayed
alone among the big brown trees and the whispering lake. Now,
however, she felt again that sudden, uprising anger, so sharp it
was pain. Turning, with a careless, impudent glance over her
shoulder, she began to trot steadily ahead in the direction of
the bridge. Behind her, she could hear them calling to her to
stop, but she did not look back. Jeanie broke into a run,
cursing her rheumatics, that made it difficult even to keep up

28

with a small child. Isabella bobbed sedately behind her, her neat curls stirred by the wind, but she looked anxious. The boards of the bridge were slippery with moss, and Marjory over-reaching herself, was unsteady on her feet as most children are. Isabella flew ahead, leaving Jeanie behind. On one side of the bridge the lake water slid into the sluice in a miniature rapid; on the other it came pouring out and down the stream in a rush of foam and brown water, swollen by the autumn rain. Marjory, reaching it, was appalled, but she could not stop; between the boards she could see the water swirling away beneath her; her feet slipped, her hands flew out, scattering the leaves. In that moment Isabella seized her, grabbing her by the skirt of her best white dress, which, made for sedate parties and no more, gave at the waist with a tearing sound. To Jeanie, panting up to them and too far away to see what had really happened it sounded like the crack of doom. Running off like that without a word! Isabella, confronted, stood helplessly in the path, her eyes filling with tears. The strength of mind that had prompted her to run after Marjory, had completely deserted her. She was incapable of defending herself. A look of bewilderment passed across her face, and the tears fell. Marjory, dancing anxiously on her toes, saw it. Her own fear had passed away completely, and she did not care for Jeanie. A new warm feeling for Isabella possessed her. Flinging herself between them she pushed Jeanie away as hard as she could.

'Leave Isy alone! Leave her alone!' she commanded, butting Jeanie fiercely with her head. A tremendous burst of courage filled her. 'You can shake Maidie as much as you like, but touch Isy, and I'll roar like a bull!'

Jeanie's wrath by this time had subsided into grumblings, and she led the way home again without shaking anybody. Rage lent wings to her feet, and temporarily banished her rheumatics, for never had she walked so fast. They passed through the gates with Isabella only just keeping up with her and Marjory, tired out by this time, stumping miserably along behind wailing. 'Wait for Maidie, Jeanie, do wait for her!' her

29

torn white dress dragging on the ground. It was really a dreadful tragedy.

Mrs. Fleming heard the story immediately on their return. Everyone in the house heard it at least six times in the course of the evening. Mr. Fleming as a last resort dived into his newspaper to avoid being told it again, and forced to give his opinion on the wilful behaviour of his younger daughter. All they could make him say was that Isabella had behaved very properly indeed, and saved her sister from what might have been a very nasty accident; but now since it was over and no harm done after all, the incident might be closed. William, busy with his map, thought so too.

'Accident! Why, she saved Maidie's life!' declared Mrs. Fleming, much agitated at the thought. She smiled fondly at Isabella, who smiled back. She was glad for once to have pleased everyone. Even Jeanie, her annoyance past, declared she had done very well. They all said something except Marjory, who was asleep upstairs, and had already forgotten; but nobody told her that this afternoon beside the lake would tumble down a hundred years and more, like a stitch dropped from time: because nobody knew.

Summer 1808

Early in the morning, when the dew lay on the grass, it was peaceful. The garden looked cool and grey. You could hear the distant sound of the sea if you kept very still, but muted, as in a dream. Marjory stood listening to it with her feet in the grass. She had come out without any shoes or stockings. Her white frock gleamed in the early light, and her arms, pale gold from the sun, were hidden in the shadows. Marjory at five years old, was a strong, well-built little girl; most of the traits lightly shown in her at three, had deepened. Her short brown hair, still untidy, had fair lights in it; her eyes, set wide apart, were dark and fearless. She was serious, self-willed, moved to sudden gusts of laughter, and just as sudden tempers. It was not a child's face, and yet, as she stood waiting for the sun to rise, she was every child that has ever been.

The heat had a strange effect on nearly everyone. They grew lazy and languid; even Jeanie did not grumble so much as usual. Isabella, her heavy curls clinging to her temples, never stirred from the garden. Marjory went down to the beach by herself. Unlike everyone else, the heat gave her energy; she grew restless, was never still. She seemed to burn like a flame herself. A hundred times a day Mrs. Fleming begged her not to move about so much. It was very provoking to have this great heat just the week she had invited her youngest niece from Edinburgh on a visit. Isabella Keith had never seen Kirkcaldy; she had met her aunt and uncle only at Edinburgh, and it had seemed a good time to return hospitality. Isabella must not expect to find such comforts as at home; the household was simple; but she loved the country and said she was fond of children, and so it was arranged.

Marjory was thinking of her cousin, as she stood in the grass. She did not much want her to come and yet she was curious. Isy said that their cousins were very fine, and that both Isabella and Nancy (whose real name was Agnes) wore silk gowns every day. Marjory wanted very much to see these but, apart from this, she thought the visit would be very tiresome. Isabella was seventeen, and what could one do with a great girl like that? Very likely if she wore fine dresses, she would go out to tea every day, and when she had visited everyone they knew in Kirkcaldy, she would go back to Edinburgh. Isy can entertain her; she is always sitting still, thought Marjory; 'I won't speak,' and she looked more obstinate than ever.

'I wish Maidie's hair were not so much of a mop,' said Mrs. Fleming later in the day, when she was setting out their best dresses, and new blue sashes, on the bed. 'Isabella always looks nice; I only wish I could say the same of Maidie.'

Marjory pretended not to hear, but she *had* heard, and she was cross. It was very unfair, she felt, that her hair did not curl. It would have been just as easy for God, if it had. She stood upon a chair and looked at herself in the mirror. Then, with a sigh, she climbed down again before anyone came in and found her. The whole house was upset because of her cousin's visit. The guest-room door stood open, and Isabella and Marjory had cut the red roses that stood in a bowl on the table. Mrs. Fleming had suggested this, and Marjory had agreed rather unwillingly, because she was reading. There was lavender in all the drawers, and here, too, the blinds were drawn and the room looked dim and cool. She tip-toed to the door and peered inside. What a pretty room! Usually the door was shut, and the furniture covered with white sheets. Now it looked perfectly ready to welcome the visitor. Marjory stood looking at everything with great admiration. Jeanie Robertson found her there when she came upstairs, followed by Isabella, to put them into their white dresses. 'Come away into your own room, then, and let me get started on ye,' said Jeanie, who was always in a hurry. Marjory came slowly. It was too hot for a best dress, best manners, best anything.

'Why are best dresses always white?' she wanted to know. Nobody told her. Mrs. Fleming thought Maidie was getting very spoilt; it was her father, reading those books and poetry to her, and telling her she understood them as well as a grown-up person. As a result it was making the child quite domineering, to her sister, and Jeanie, and everyone else. Perhaps it was time to send her to school, for it was true she was very forward, and already, at five, could do eight-year-old Isabella's lessons quicker than she. That again was not good for her; but what could one do? She had to teach them together. Looking at Maidie, she frowned, then pushed the problem to the back of her mind. The most immediate thing was to keep her quiet and still until their cousin came. They looked very nice, hand in hand, and Marjory's hair was neatly brushed. Pleased, she tucked a pink rose into each sash, and sent Marjory into the library for a book.

Turning the door knob gently with both hands, she went in. It was quiet in here too, and the shadow of the leaves rippled on the ceiling like water. There was a globe in the centre of the room. Marjory brushed it lightly with her finger in passing; as lightly as an accident, because she was not meant to touch it. It spun with a soft whirring sound in the silent room. Red, blue, green, the countries and the oceans flashed by. William took the outline of his maps from the globe. When she had watched it move slower and slower, until it stopped, she turned to the books. They rose from floor to ceiling, just as they did in Mr. Parcel's shop, but much tidier. The room was sweet with the scent of leather. Looking round she wondered whether, if you read every book, and never once skipped, you would know everything in the world. From far away, in another world, she heard her mother call:

'Maidie! make haste, or they will be here before you.'

Of course, Papa had driven to Kinghorn to meet cousin Isabella. They would be back before she had found a book to read, if she did not hurry. She *must* find a book. It became suddenly

C
33

very important. Standing there in the dim, rustling room, in her stiff white dress with the high waist and new puffed sleeves, she was suddenly afraid. For the first time since babyhood she wanted to run to her mother, and hide her head in her lap. She did not want them to come. It was just as if, in her mind, a door had burst open, and she had peeped inside, into a world of strange, new sensations. She wanted to cling to the things she had known all her life. She wanted to be safe. So she stood forlornly beside the globe and her hands, when she pressed them together, shook. At the sound of the door opening she started, and looked round with wide eyes; but it was only her mother, come to call her outside.

'We will walk down into the archway, and see them come. The carriage is sure to stop there,' she said, and added, 'You look pale, my love, it must be the heat.'

'Yes,' said Marjory, hanging her head. As they went out she slipped her hand into her mother's. 'Poor mother,' she thought. She did not know why she should think this. When they stepped out of the house they could feel the heat rise to meet them. They stood just inside the archway, out of the sun. William was there too, looking very tidy and talking a great deal. Presently they heard the sound of hooves; there was not much traffic in the High Street at that hour, and no mail coach was expected. It could only be Papa. The carriage stopped and there he was; the children ran from under the arch to watch him help cousin Isabella out of the carriage; only one of them drew back.

Marjory never forgot the first time she saw Isabella Keith, that hot, bright afternoon in summer. Behind her the sky burnt blue as a peacock's tail, and the houses shimmered. Only the shadow under the arch was very black and cool. Isabella stood there, laughing, her white dress gathered into her hands. She had tossed back her white straw bonnet and there was one red rose in her hair. She had a trick of raising her eyebrows when she smiled and her eyes were very blue, clear, and yet sharp. There was a sharpness too in her movements. For a minute she stood without speaking, her dancing eyes taking them in at a glance, then she came forward and kissed her aunt. She was not very tall and had almost to stand on her toes to do it. 'Isabella, my dear!' exclaimed Mrs. Fleming, a little bewildered. Her niece had been in the school room, a quiet, rather plump girl, when she last visited Edinburgh. This slender, lovely creature laughing up at her from a wide curtsey, was like a stranger. Her curls swept forward, glinting red in the sun.

There was a scurry, a flash of white across the path. Marjory was gone without even waiting to greet her cousin. It was most rude. She had run indoors almost as if she was afraid, which was plainly ridiculous in such a forward child. Mrs. Fleming sighed and presented her eldest daughter instead; good, meek Isabella, who would certainly show her cousin to her room.

'Marjory is a little difficult, I'm afraid,' she said, half laughing. 'I always say her father is too proud of her. He spoils her.'

Marjory, crouched at the top of the stairs with her head between the banisters, sighed. She could not quite make out the words, but she knew her mother was not pleased. It was rather rude to run away like that, she supposed; she did not know why she had done it. She had never seen anyone like Isabella before; she was not sour and cross, like Jeanie, nor busy like her mother; she looked as if she laughed a great deal. Marjory sat on the top step with her chin in her hands. She frowned, considering. Isabella Keith was very romantic; she ought to be in a story, and marry after a great many difficulties and then live happily for ever.

There was a rustle in the passage behind her. She turned. Isabella stood there, laughing, swinging her bonnet by the strings.

'Well, cousin Marjory!' she said, in her soft, rather grave voice. 'Don't you want to speak to me?'

Marjory stared at her. She climbed to her feet and leaned against the banisters while she thought this out.

'Yes, I do,' she said, nodding her head; and added at once, 'I think so, at least.'

Isabella nodded too. She seemed to understand. She said:
'Will you come to my room? There's a present for you in the trunk.'

Marjory stiffened.

'I won't come for that,' she said, coldly. There was silence. 'Thank you, cousin Isabella,' she added in a very small voice.

Isabella held out her hand.

'I am sorry,' she said. 'I was stupid, but it was not my meaning. The present was in any case, you know. But you must only come and see me if you like me.'

Marjory jumped down two stairs and then up again, because she was excited. Nobody had spoken to her before as if she was really grown up herself and could understand things. Isabella was different; perhaps they could really be friends. Marjory had never had a friend. She played with other children, but she had never confided in them. Why, she knew as much as they did. She was one of those people who always seek a deeper, finer mind. Now, wondering, her cheeks grew pink. She held out her own hand.

'I do like you, cousin Isabella, indeed I do,' she said, very earnestly. Her eyes looked very big.

'Then we'll be friends,' said Isabella, in a decided voice. She dropped down on the step beside Marjory like a flower in her white dress. 'But you must call me Isa, as they do at home. That's better than "cousin Isabella" is it not?'

'Oh yes,' said Marjory gratefully, and was child enough to ask, 'Will William and Isy call you that too?'

'Of course,' said Miss Keith, decidedly. 'It's my name, you know. Are you never called anything else but Marjory?'

She was silent. She did not dare say that they called her Maidie, in case her cousin should think it stupid, and suddenly remembered that she was five years old. Isa Keith was seventeen and quite grown up. So Marjory sighed, and did not own that she was Maidie, too. Isabella, however, made a decision.

'I shall call you Madgie!' she declared, sweeping up from the stairs again with a great rustling. Marjory nodded. She felt sure that Isa was right. From then on to the end of her life,

humbly, hopefully, striving beyond her limits to be like her,
she was sure that her cousin was right.

It was strange how soon the house became accustomed to
the intrusion of the lovely, surprising Isabella. She went upstairs and down, and was welcome everywhere. Even Jeanie
Robertson petted her. The silk dresses were unpacked and
hung in the closet, and there were stiff starched muslins too,
with frills and ribbons to be pressed and inserted at the waist.
Isabella's nightgowns had real lace on them. All these strange
things hung in Jeanie's room and made it much gayer and
brighter than ever before. Isabella brought yards of taffeta and
silk, and talk of the newest fashions, to her aunt, and Mrs.
Fleming was grateful. Sometimes she missed the bustle of
Edinburgh sadly. Yet Isabella thought very little of clothes in
general. 'One may as well have something pretty as not,' she
wisely said, and gave it no further thought, though she
laughed to find Marjory peeping into the closet to admire her
cousin's best dress, which was *not* white muslin, but pale blue
taffeta. Isabella did not lie in bed late like a fine lady; she was
up and out nearly as early as Marjory in the cool summer
mornings before the sun had risen. Hand in hand, they walked
down to the beach. Marjory, her thoughts locked up behind her
fierce, rather obstinate little face, opened like a flower to the
sun. She suddenly showed a longing for trust and for affection.
She had found, at last, someone in whom she was willing to confide, someone who listened, who neither laughed nor suggested
she was too young to trouble her head with such thoughts.
Marjory's head was constantly troubled with thoughts of every
kind on every subject. She said, 'What's that, and why?' to life,
stretching her mind to reach new knowledge each day. It came
to her early, too soon to be borne, that she was *herself*, a person,
not any child; only part of her belonged to her sister, her
mother. The rest was herself and untouchable. She was not an
unhappy child, but a lonely one; it was the price she paid for
what was in her. Her family loved her; her father in particular
thought her clever beyond the average. But her father was out
a great part of the day. It was her mother who had to cope

with her sudden fits of temper, her inability—or refusal—to do her everyday lessons. She burrowed deep into great books out of her father's shelves that were not meant for children to read, and could not do the simplest sum in mathematics. Her writing was careless, and she queried everything she was told, constantly asking for more and more. Mrs. Fleming, occupied with the house, set the children their tasks and marked them either right or wrong. (Isabella did hers carefully, conscientiously, and was finished.) She had not time to answer Marjory's questions, and frequently could not. In any case, no child of five should want to know so much. Mrs. Fleming, in a hurry, put it down to a precocity gained by too much reading and told her not to show off. If her father encouraged her in it, no-one else should. When she had not her nose in a book, she was a gay, natural, careless child, up to more tricks than her slower sister, whom she dominated. No, said Mrs. Fleming, to reassure herself, there was nothing strange about Marjory, only that she was getting out of hand and it might be as well to think about sending her to school.

Isabella Keith, gay, clever, so young and so sure, was pleased with her cousin. She was just grown-up, and still had a joy in the unusual; she was not afraid of it as her elders were. She saw at once in Marjory a fine mind, and was wise enough to treat the child with respect, not as an inferior being. Marjory, sensing approval, opened her heart even wider. She came running to Isa whenever she could. Standing on the beach with her toes buried in the sands, her eyes glad and fearless, she pleaded:

'Don't go home, Isa. Stay here with me.'

The gulls circled and wheeled in the blue sky above them. The small waves kissed where they touched the shore. Isa, laughing as the wind tugged at her curls, was silent. She looked back at Marjory, whose face had clouded. Standing in the sand with her dress tucked into her sash to be out of the way, she looked rather small and sad.

'Come!' said Isa, holding out her hand. 'Don't spoil the present with the future, Muff. I'm not gone yet.'

Marjory laughed too. Then stumping up the sandy path behind Isa, she sighed. To get older was dreadful; she wished she might always stay here, on the shore with Isa. If Isa were there she would always be good. Glancing sideways, she saw that her cousin, too, was quiet; she was frowning.

'What are you thinking about, Isa?'

Taking her hand, Isabella began to run. She looked merry again, as if her mind were made up. When they reached the top of the hill she turned, and said in her gay, clear voice:

'Why, about you.'

A week later, the decision, sprung almost carelessly into her mind, had become firm. It was her habit, when the children were in bed, and Mrs. Fleming occupied with the supper, to take a walk in the garden with her uncle. It was the only time she could see him. In the evening, when the big stars came out and the sweet scented dusk crept in from the sea, she felt at peace. It was easy, then, to talk. She could not see his face, nor he hers. Only her dress gleamed white, like the two rose-bushes beside the door. She had tied her curls back with blue ribbons and looked grave, composed. Her voice remained aloof, when she made her request. She knew, she said quickly, that they had been thinking of sending Marjory to school (like a thorn, it pricked through the conversation every day, turn it how they would). He refused to make such a big decision quickly. Mrs. Fleming, who knew how swiftly she was losing authority with the child, pressed the matter a little each day. Send away Marjory, the gay, pert creature who was the only one to make him laugh? Here was Isabella taking her aunt's part. It was a good plan, she was saying; the child was quick and would benefit from a change. 'Let her,' said Isabella, carelessly pulling leaves from the currant-bushes. 'Let her come back to Edinburgh with me.' She leaned forward, earnestly. 'Truly you will not regret it. I will care for her as if she were my own.'

In the silence, her words seemed to flutter between them like the white-winged moths over the rose-bushes. He thought of Edinburgh; the great house richer than his own; Marjory would have books, music, painting, and a house full of cousins. She would be among friends; Isa she loved already. He looked at his niece, standing very still in her wide white dress, with something shining round her neck; a little cross on a silver chain. Very young she looked, and grave; yet he could trust her, in spite of her youth. So, one day, would his Maidie stand, needing no better pattern.

'We will see what your aunt says,' was his answer; and she knew that it was settled.

There were letters to Edinburgh, by each mail that rattled into Kirkcaldy, but in essentials the thing was done. The hot weather dissolved into rain. Round, heavy drops splashed down on the parched green leaves. Jeanie and Mrs. Fleming conferred together over the big black trunk that now stood in the nursery, and was to go with Marjory to Edinburgh. Asked to select what she liked best, she would have filled it up with books, and was prevented. Instead, she carefully put in three rather battered wooden dolls, and would not take her best one, which was of wax and had real hair. Since her aunt Keith had sent it to her, Mrs. Fleming was vexed, but Marjory would not give in. It had no character in her eyes, and it was their fault, because they had wrapped it up in silver paper on the top shelf of the cupboard, and only let her play with it when it rained, or visitors came. How could she love it, when the first longing had been quenched? So she took her wooden dolls, with smiling painted faces, and a very small fan, and her best amber beads, and I know not what else besides. Then she wanted to take her porridge plate and spoon; both were of porcelain, with a mauvy pattern, and Marjory liked them. In vain, her mother declared she would get one as good at her aunt's; it would break on the way, and be tiresome. The wrangle began at the dinner-table a few days before she left, and might have gone on for ever if her father had not looked up and said, 'Let the child take it!' Marjory looked back at him gratefully; then smiled brilliantly, inscrutably, at her mother.

Day by day, the trunk filled up. She did not take all her dresses, for many were given away. Mrs. Fleming, after discussion with her, agreed that she could buy what was needful in Edinburgh. One new thing she did have before she left: a warm travelling-cloak like her mother's, lined with scarlet. Marjory made a scene in the shop, because it was not also edged with fur. This time her father was not at hand to support her, and the cloak remained without fur. The hot summer days had gone, never to return; autumn swept slowly over the woods and fields and the air was sharp and scented with wet leaves. When they went round the lake in Raith grounds, they walked quickly. The evenings drew in; lamps were lit earlier, and fires were laid.

Like a dream, the last day had past. The evening came. She ate bread and jam and drank her milk from her own silver mug, perched beside her sister Isabella as she had always done. William teased her, and made her laugh by stories of what he had done at school; this, too, was the same. Jeanie, grumbling, drew close the heavy curtains, and shut out the night, as if she had some personal spite against it. In the drawing-room her parents sat beside the fire, and Isa with them. Her father was reading. Marjory, pushing away her plate, wriggled off her chair and went to sit on his knee. She knew he admired her. Like Isabella he sensed the power of her mind, hidden deceptively in her child's body; a child and yet a personality. It was the strangeness of these two selves that was entrancing. At one moment, laughing, rushing up and down the room after her brother and sister, she was just any little girl, perhaps noisier, and plainer than most; the next, her game over, she came back, quiet, vivid.

Her father was proud, for this was his child; down through the years had come this quick, fantastic streak of Highland blood. It had not died out but had settled in Marjory. The other two were an equal balance of Rae and Fleming, each line traced easily to one or other parent. Who could trace in Marjory anything that he knew? She was different, and would suffer for it; better perhaps for her to go among strangers, whom she had chosen instinctively as her own. The knowledge of this made him bend his head close to hers, as she sat on his knee, and whisper, his breath stirring her short-cropped hair:

'If you don't settle with your cousins, Maidie, you may come home: but, if you're happy there, you shall stay. I cannot do more for you.'

She looked up at him with confidence, her hands folded in her lap.

'Yes, papa,' she whispered, as lightly as he. 'I will remember.'

When Jeanie Robertson came in to call her to bed, she slipped off his knee, without waiting to be called twice. Only, when he kissed her good-bye she clung to him a little and sighed.

Isabella, who found her mother's daily task sufficiently hard, was not moved to envy. Indeed, in Marjory's place she would have been frankly scared. This young person, however, was not put out at all. Would she not have Isa with her? 'It's wickedness pure and simple,' was Jeanie's verdict, when she had angled in vain for Marjory to say she was sorry to leave her. 'Any natural child would be crying her eyes out, leaving her home and all her friends behind her, to go off Lord knows where with a cousin who's no more than a child herself!' and she sniffed very loudly to show what she thought of Miss Isabella Keith.

'The Lord *does* know where!' retorted Marjory, sitting straight up in bed. 'We're going to Edinburgh.'

She lay down again very quickly, for Jeanie looked extremely cross, and her shadow flickered menacingly up the wall. Soon she stumped out of the room, taking the candle with her. There was silence, and a smothered giggle from Isabella, who had come to bed early on Marjory's last evening, and was therefore wide awake.

'You're a strange girl, Maidie,' she whispered, half curiously, half admiringly, across the void between the two beds. 'Aren't you sorry to leave *anything*?'

'Yes, I am,' said Marjory, in a burst of feeling. 'I'm sorry to leave papa, and you, and the house, and Raith, and *everything*.

But not Jeanie. She's cross, and she scratches when she washes you. Besides, she *asks*, so.'

There was a pause.

'Isy,' said Marjory at last, nearly asleep. 'There's something else I'm sorry about too.'

'Yes?' Isabella whispered back, interested. 'What is it?'

Marjory yawned and pulled herself back from the fringe of sleep to impart this information, which had weighed upon her since the afternoon.

'Mr. Parcel's shop,' she said, and this time fell asleep almost before the words were out of her mouth.

Isabella was left alone in the dark, waiting an explanation. She had not the slightest idea what her sister was talking about.

They were up early the next day, and yet her father had left the house before them, and was gone off on business. Marjory was disappointed, although he had left some money for her in a brown purse; it was put by her plate at breakfast. She had never had money of her own to spend before and felt extremely grand.

'Take care of it then,' said her mother, who did not entirely approve. Her own parting-gift was a prayer book. 'You had better give it to Isa, and let her keep it for you, or else you will squander it in the town, I'm afraid.'

Marjory snatched it off the table, and put it in her lap. Oh, this power that older people had over you! 'It's mine, my own,' she whispered to herself, with fiery cheeks, as she ate her porridge off an unfamiliar white plate because her own was packed. The black trunk containing all her worldly possessions had been corded up and brought down into the passage outside the kitchen. Jeanie Robertson got Mr. Parcel's assistant, a pale, thin youth, to help the coachman lift it on to the coach. This came rumbling down the High Street ten minutes before it was expected, which put everyone into a flurry. Only Isa stood calmly by, wrapped in a white cloak, the hood lined with ermine; it made her look like a fairy, Marjory thought. She did not get in the least alarmed, and turned out to be right, for the coach stopped in Kirkcaldy for nearly half an hour, while mail was taken off and on, passengers arrived and went off again for a drink. The sun was bright, but the wind was cold. 'A real autumn day,' said Jeanie, looking gratified. Marjory hopped up and down on the doorstep, and wished they might be off. Her mother kept near her, giving her stray pieces of advice and odd messages whenever she had nothing else to do. Marjory would rather have been beside William, talking familiarly, as man to man, with the coachman, who was his friend. Isabella kept just inside the door; Jeanie had not found time to do her curls that morning, and she looked, and felt, untidy.

At last the moment came. Marjory clung to her mother in a sudden burst of affection and a secret guilt, because she could not help being glad to go with Isa. 'I'll write you, Mud,' she promised. 'And Isy too.' Isabella looked pleased. Marjory and Isa climbed into the coach and everyone, smiling indulgently, allowed the child to lean from the small window to give her mother a last kiss.

There was a sudden jolt, the clash of hooves on the cobbled street, and they were off. Marjory sat very still and straight beside Isa. For the first time she felt a little afraid; a lump came into her throat. It was not so much a fear of leaving home—and, in a sense, she had left it for ever—but it was a strange feeling that, as she grew, grew with her. It was as if a door opened, and in a flash she *felt* what was about to happen. Knowledge rushed upon her, sickening her, because it was inevitable. Yet it only lasted a moment; she could not have said what it was she learnt in that flash; it left only a vague impression behind, as a dream does. So, perhaps, she knew she had shut her home out of her life, even if she returned. The world she would grasp in exchange was still unknown.

It was not long before they reached Kinghorn, and the sea lapped almost up to the road. Here they embarked on a boat to take them across the Firth, and here too Isa bent her head and whispered to Marjory an intimate but necessary question.

Marjory shook her head, but she was impressed. Her mother would never have said such a thing before people. Being one of those who are born with a disregard for convention, she admired Isa for not caring. All the people from the coach got on board the boat, and a good bit of the mail as well. They smiled at Marjory, seeing a child in a scarlet cloak holding on to her companion's hand. She, being of a dignified nature, decided that strangers ought not to smile at a person they did not even know, and turned away her head. A child does not *think* of itself as a child, now or in 1808, and Marjory less than most. Isa gave her biscuit and a slice of cake, and Marjory was pleased.

Leith seemed very much like Kinghorn as they approached it, but it was the other side of the Firth. Marjory, with admirable lack of geography and a great sense of drama, decided that she had left her native land behind, and was now on foreign shores, with no-one but Isa to protect her. This idea pleased her, and made her less tired and cold. At Leith, they had a surprise; a particularly pleasant one to Isabella, who was also cold and had no fancies to counteract it. Her brother Willie had come all the way in the carriage to meet them, and brought with him Charles Balfour, who lived in the Square next to the Keiths, and had grown up with them. He was tall, had thick brown hair and merry eyes, and Isabella was glad they had come. Willie was her favourite brother, and she had missed her home. Visits were not to be lightly undertaken, especially over the treacherous sea, and she had been away two months. She had found the household at Kirkcaldy dull compared with her own home, filled with brothers and sisters and friends, all coming and going, and laughing among themselves. She had grown fond of her uncle; her aunt she thought serious and preoccupied, and difficult to know.

Certainly she had brought the best of the visit back with her. Under the cloak, her hand tightened on Marjory's. What big eyes the child had! She stood gravely beside her cousin, looking at Willie, and saying nothing.

Isa introduced her. Charles bowed at once, and shook hands

very formally. 'Good day, Miss Fleming,' he said gravely. Marjory had no experience of teasing at home; she dominated her sister, and her father never laughed at her. She thought Charles amiable and polite and responded with her best curtsey. Willie, on the contrary, laughed at her.

'That's a queer little fish you've hooked out of the sea!' he said to his sister. The blood flew into Marjory's cheeks. She looked dismayed. Isabella frowned at Willie, but she could not help laughing. When he had gone off to see about their luggage, and get it put into the carriage, Marjory recovered; some of her lost dignity returned.

'It's not very polite for a gentleman to laugh at a lady, is it?' she demanded, hurt. Isa shook her head, although she was laughing too. She did not attempt an explanation then; the child was tired, and would soon learn to be teased when they got home; but it was too bad of Willie to start so soon. He might know she was not used to it. Only Mr. Balfour seemed properly to understand.

'Indeed it is not, Miss Fleming,' he said, just as gravely as before, though little specks of light danced in his eyes and made them twinkle. 'Pray let me counsel you to take no notice of that rude fellow, but come with me to the carriage.'

Isa began to laugh again at this, but Marjory was glad. She wished very much that Mr. Balfour was her cousin and not Willie. It was so nice to be treated with consideration, just as if she were grown up. When they reached the carriage, she saw that the step was very high, *much* too high. It was most awkward, indeed it was, and Isa had remained behind to wait for the awful Willie. Somewhere inside her a very small girl, who was not the *real* Marjory, burst into tears. Again Mr. Balfour came gallantly to the rescue, and tragedy was averted.

'Allow me!' he said politely, and lifted her up as if it was the most natural thing in the world. A little breathless, she found herself seated on the shiny leather seat of the Keiths' private carriage, which Marjory considered a great joy of luxury. Her feet did not quite touch the floor, so she wriggled forward until they did, and said in her firm, light voice:

'Mr. Balfour, you are very kind. If it would please you, you can call me Marjory.'

Mr. Balfour bowed again, and his eyes twinkled more than ever. 'Madam, you do me too much honour!' he said, exactly as they did in a book she had read, at home. Of course, this time she knew he was teasing her; she joined in with her own clear laugh, and tipped herself back in the seat. It was funny, she thought, not rude like being called a fish; and he said she must call him Charles, as everyone did. Then they would really be friends.

'I wish you were my cousin, I do indeed,' she said. 'For Willie is a rude boy; besides, I like you the best.'

'I'm glad you like me,' he said, and this time he too was serious. He leaned down to her because she was smaller than he and his voice was kind. 'Willie does not mean to be rude, Marjory. He was teasing you because he liked you. Nobody troubles to tease anyone they dislike, or are indifferent to; and you must not mind it, but learn to laugh back. That's the way to go on!'

'Oh!' said Marjory, surprised. She considered this. 'I will try,' she decided, adding a little anxiously. 'But I hope that all the Keiths are not so fond of it as he.'

Charles laughed; shook her by the hand and said she was a good girl, which made her feel proud. Isabella and Willie arrived, having been delayed over the luggage, and climbed into the carriage. The sun had gone down in a mist of purple over the sea, and the night came on. It was very secure to be in the carriage, riding to Edinburgh and to have made a friend in this new life already. She would not feel nearly so strange. Leaning against Isa, she closed her eyes. Isa had thrown back the hood of her cloak, and the wind stirred her curls very lightly. She too was glad to be here, listening to the news from home and learning that they had missed her. They talked and laughed while Marjory slept and the carriage rocked on through the night.

A little later Marjory woke; she lay with the eyes closed, while the talk flowed round her. She heard Isa's soft warm voice and Willie's laugh. Presently Charles spoke; then Willie, in the midst of an argument cried out, 'Well, but you are not a married man, and that's the difference....'

Marjory sat up, very wide awake in an instant.

'Oh, you *should* be married!' she exclaimed. 'You are so nice!'

With this, being still very sleepy, she gave a big yawn and rubbed her eyes. Isa said, 'Hush, Marjory,' but the boys laughed. Mr. Balfour took her hand and said:

'Perhaps you will do me the honour of marrying me then, to save me from further disgrace!'

Marjory swung her feet to and fro, and yawned again. 'Really, Charles, how ridiculous!' they said and then, 'The child is half asleep.' But she was not. That is, her eyes would not keep open, but she knew very well what was going on round her, and felt perfectly satisfied. It was nice to be driving along in a carriage like a fine lady and receiving a proposal of marriage into the bargain. She must remember to tell Isy all about it when she wrote home, for Isy, although the eldest, had never had such a thing happen in her life.

It was quite dark when they reached Edinburgh, and well past Marjory's bedtime, so she saw little of the town where she was to spend the three happiest years of her life, indeed, the whole of it, for the rest was but a shadow in comparison, a winding up of what had been. The carriage turned into Charlotte Square, and there it was, on the corner of the square and North Charlotte Street, a big, tall, wide-windowed house with a lamp above the door. She climbed down from the carriage, and stood waiting for Isa. Looking up at it for the first time, the light from the lamp falling in her eyes, she *felt* that it was home. This house, too, had a secret, wide-awake look, as if it had in some queer way been waiting for this day, when the heavy door would fly open to admit a child in a crumpled dress, a child who stood breathless under the swinging lamp, because this was her cousin's house, and a dream made suddenly true. Then, as Isa pushed her gently up the steps, she wanted to run away. The first and last time, how mixed together they are; now, when she stepped over the threshold into the warm hall, lighted with white wax tapers and scented with wood fires and polish, she knew her great moment was over. Time, from now onwards, was pushing her towards the last time; she was caught. These feelings struggled inside her for expression as she stood rather timidly on the soft carpet at No. 1 North Charlotte Street. Her aunt Keith rustled down the stairs to meet her, dressed in burgundy coloured silk, as fine as possible. She looked younger, gayer, than her sister, though she had so many grown-up children; only her eyes, deep and blue, like her daughter Isa's, gave her away, for they held a lifetime of experience and humour. Now, in an instant her swift look flew to Marjory; she took in at once the sturdy face, the over-sensitive mouth, the wide wonder of her intent gaze; and in an instant guessed much of the smouldering spirit that was in her; Isa, watching, saw something between pity and dismay flash into her mother's eyes, and wondered. Sweeping across the hall, she put both her hands on the child's shoulders, tilted her face to the light.

'How did my sister come by you, you changeling?' she said, so swiftly that Marjory caught only the tone, tender, half admiring. She stood still, instead of wrenching away as she generally did when touched, unbidden, by strangers. Her aunt had not spoken to her as a child, altering her voice, but as woman to woman. Marjory, wondering, smiled uncertainly. Two dimples appeared; the taut, unearthly look vanished; she was five years old again and sleepy. Marianne Keith, with a look that was nearly relief, caught her up and kissed her.

'Well, Marjory!' she said and sighed. 'You've had a long journey, my love, and must be tired. And hungry. Isa will take you upstairs—the blue closet, Isa, next to yours. I'll come to you presently, Marjory, your uncle has visitors.'

She rustled up the stairs again, this time with Marjory's hand tucked securely into hers; the child clutched it so tight that the rings hurt her palm. At the drawing-room door she paused; kissed her niece good night, and put the hand gently into Isa's.

'Take her to bed,' she said firmly, and was gone.

D 49

★ *Part One* ★

Up, up, up; four flights of low, crimson-carpeted stairs. Up
to the top of the house. The Keith children still slept in their
old nurseries, and they had a nurse too, who came bustling out
into the passage to meet Isabella. Marjory stood still. Ah, how
different from sour Jeanie Robertson with her black clothes
and brooches that scratched! Nan was small and round and
smiling; she had grey hair screwed into a no-nonsense-about-it
sort of bun, and eyes as sharp as flints, and nearly as grey. All
her wrinkles were from laughing and she wore gay print
dresses scented with lavender. Isa was in her arms in a moment,
though she was tall and Nan so little. Marjory only knew that
she was tired, and had found someone safe and good. Without
waiting to be introduced she ran into Nan's arms; hid her face
and said she was *so* sleepy, because she knew that this would
be understood. Wise or stupid or brilliant, what did Nan care?
Isa might be clever, and a lovely young lady, but she should
have known better than to keep a child up so much beyond
bedtime, journey or no journey. Nan scolded cheerfully away
while she undressed Marjory, and her grumbling passed lightly
over the child's nodding head and became mingled with the
twinkling candles, and warm water, and the milk they gave her
to drink. The last thing she clung to in this waking world was
Isa's hand, she dropped asleep long before they carried her
into bed and took the candlestick away.

Isa, closing the door softly, came down the stairs, and
stopped outside her mother's room. Now, with no child to offset
her, she looked younger, a child herself. Her eyes held bewilderment, and a little doubt. For a moment, uncertain, she paused,
her hand on the door; then, tossing her head, she walked in.
The room was warm, lit with candles like stars. Freed at last
from her visitors, Marianne was curled up on the settee, a rug
over her feet. Isabella dutifully came over to the settee and
pressed her lips lightly against her mother's cheek; something
in this custom, as old as her childhood, gave her confidence. She
burst out, 'Mamma, you . . . why did you look so strange just
now?'

There was silence, while Marianne tried, suddenly, to push

Isa from her mind as she had seen her, day in and year in, since she first was laid, squalling, in her arms. She thought of her now as a person, a woman, not as a child. She said: 'Isa, don't *force* Marjory. Be gentle with her always. You're sure that you want to look after the child yourself? We could get a governess. . . .'

Isa's head tilted a little. She felt no ties of relationship, on the contrary. She felt independent, sure. Her foot tapped impatiently on the floor.

'Mamma, I told you before. I want to look after Marjory.' Her voice was clear, sharp, with the impatience, the sureness of youth. 'She's clever, and besides; it will do us both good. She isn't an ordinary child.'

'I saw that.' Marianne laughed, but her voice was sharp too. Why did the children think one a fool? They gave one credit for nothing. Then she looked at Isa. No, Isa was not like that; Isa was gentle and good, she had taken this fancy to look after her cousin, and she would do it. She was not fierce, sharp-tongued, like Nancy, but there was no weakness in her either. A tremendous love and pride surged up in her, but she did not show it. She said, almost carelessly:

'I would not have expected Isabella to have such a child! Why! she feels every breath of wind like a gale. One sees it in her face. She is like the princess in the fairy tale who slept on the pea, and felt it through seven mattresses!' She paused. 'It isn't a happy state for a child.'

'No,' said Isa, softly; thinking of Marjory upstairs, she drew in her breath. It came to her what a big thing she had done. For the first time she realized that a child, even so young, is a person; not just the creature of its elders, to be blown through life by their whims. Only a very small part of Marjory belonged to her. The rest came from who knows how far back? These things together, made her. Isa felt afraid. Dropping down by the settee with a swift rustle of taffeta, she looked up at her mother, feeling for strength, and in that moment became a child again.

'Help me, Mamma,' she whispered.

Marianne, half shyly, put out her hand. Nancy would have pushed it away at once, but Isa took it. Her daughters, growing, had shocked her by their hardness, their lack of convention. They turned away on purpose from the support she offered them. She had done it herself, years before; so time, circling, brings back the suffering we inflict. She had been patient. Now, when Isa needed her, she leaned to her, gently, longing to help.

'You *can* do it, Isa,' she said, and her voice was strong. 'They don't—I can swear my sister does not understand this child; she never was one for fancies and feelings. But if Marjory loves you, you can give her all that she needs. You can do it.'

'Can I?' said Isa, with shining eyes. She clung to her mother, pulling strength from her, and purpose. They sat still. Somewhere in the house came the dull metallic sound of a gong. Isa flew up from the settee. Her spirits soared. Before leaving the room, she kissed her mother, but this time it was a real kiss. The swift change of mood was part of her youth. A moment before, kneeling close to the settee, she had seemed hopeless. Now, nothing was impossible. She ran, singing, up the stairs. It was dark in the corridor. Gently, holding her breath, she pushed open Marjory's door. The room was washed in the pale uncertain glow of the night-light, which stood in a saucer at the foot of the bed, and had almost burnt itself out. The child lay on her side, and her face, in sleep, was strangely beautiful, yet empty. Where had her spirit flown? Isa, watching, felt the doubts, the fears of her own inadequacy, rush back upon her. She clenched her hands.

'Oh God, somebody, help me,' she pleaded, with parted lips, over the sleeping Marjory.

The night-light, springing up with a hiss in a last burst of glory, sank back, and the flame went out.

PART II

PART II

Edinburgh:
Autumn 1808—Spring 1809

S he woke early. This happened every day; and every day she opened her eyes with the same sense of relief to find herself in Edinburgh. Sitting up in bed she gazed round the room; it *was* her room. She shared it with no-one, as she did at home. On the wall over the bed was a picture of a beautiful winged horse that Isa said was called Pegasus. Once it had hung in the passage, but Marjory liked it so much, she had been allowed to have it in her own room, although Nancy had tossed her head, and called her a spoilt brat. Marjory was secretly afraid of her cousin Nancy. She had sharp slanting green eyes, and when she smiled her eyebrows went up very slightly at the corners, which gave her a scornful air. All the same, she could not leave her alone; she was fascinated. What was worse, Nancy knew it. She teased till Marjory's nerves came close to breaking point, and Isa threatened to turn her from the room; then surprisingly, she was charming. Oh, how nice Nancy could be! Marjory wished she would be like that always and loved her sincerely.

Then there was Willie. Marjory was grown so used to Nancy's taunts, she turned to Willie's plain, boyish teasing with relief. She understood it. He had a gay careless manner, and if she really needed help, she would as soon come running to him as anyone. One day, finding her howling on the stairs because she had tipped Isa's ink bottle into her lap, and Nancy would scold, he'd taken her part fiercely. He said it was a shame to scare the child out of her wits for one spoiled dress, and

Nancy was an old dragon. Marjory loved him for always after that. Besides, she teased him equally much; they plagued each other continually and were the best of friends. It was quite different with James. He was older than Willie, very grave and silent, with a slightly sardonic smile which disconcerted Marjory. He hardly ever spoke to her, and this annoyed her greatly, for she liked attention. James was studying medicine, and he had a room full of extremely dry books. Unfortunately, Marjory showed off in front of him. She did not know it, but she became noisier, more boisterous, when he entered the room. She ran up and down the passage like a mad thing while he was studying, screaming and sliding on the polished floor. Her cheeks flamed pink; her hands clenched. He would *have* to notice her. He opened the door quite suddenly, and stood looking at her. Then, in a voice of thunder, he said, 'Girl, make less noise!' and went inside again. Marjory's mouth opened wide in surprise. She never forgot it.

Every morning, waking early, she lay thinking about these things; her cousins, and the big house they lived in. It *was* a grand house, she decided. Her room, although small, was beautifully furnished. Besides the bed, and all the ordinary furniture, there was a tiny writing-table with a blue quill pen in the tray, and a castor full of sand. Marjory, the first day, heaved a big sigh. It was just what she had always wanted. She liked to stroke the quill, and whisper 'Mine'.

All the same, when Isa suggested she should use it to write a letter home, she shook her head. She hated writing letters. Isy had written her several, and she knew she was bad not to answer, but then she had so much to do. There was not nearly so much to do at Kirkcaldy. To-day, for instance, was Thursday. On that day, her aunt stayed in and received visitors. Marjory wore a very pretty new dress that Isa bought her. Muslin, though 'best' at home, was not nearly fine enough for Edinburgh. This was lace, with an underskirt of pale blue silk, and pale blue ribbons inserted at the waist. Nancy said she looked like a doll, but for once Marjory was not perturbed. She knew from what other people said that she looked very nice.

'People who are not pretty can be interesting,' she told Nancy, who said she was getting to be a regular little prig.

Besides her new dress, Thursday was nice because there were cakes for tea. Marjory, who had lived plainly at home, liked food as much as most children. Thinking about it, made her jump out of bed and run to the window to see what kind of weather it was going to be. The sky was grey and wintry, but it was not raining. Isa taught Marjory every day for two hours, at present; but when she was six it would be for longer. She read poetry, history, plays. Marjory sat opposite her cousin, with her eyes as round as saucers, and took in what she could. Isa was very clever, she thought. Sometimes they did arithmetic, and always, every day, there was a writing lesson. This was the worst trial she had to bear. She simply hated copying pious phrases out of a nasty little grey book, in a big round hand. It cast a cloud over even Thursday morning, and made her pull a face while Isa was brushing her hair.

'If the wind changes now, you will stay like that,' Isa told her; Nana had told *her*. Marjory burst out laughing. Because Isa helped her to dress, she was sometimes late herself. However, this morning, she was up early and came downstairs, with Marjory holding her hand and feeling extremely proud.

Willie and Nancy were eating their porridge already, and Marjory's own plate and spoon had been laid next to Nancy instead of Isa. This was a tragedy and made her turn quite pale.

'Come and sit down, and stop looking as if you'd seen a ghost,' commanded Nancy, sipping coffee and warming her hands on the cup.

Marjory stared at Nancy. Her knees trembled, and she was frightened. Without a word she snatched up her plate and spoon, and marched round to the other side of the table close to Isa.

'No, I won't,' she said, in a sort of gasp. Nancy looked very fierce at this; but Willie said approvingly:

'That's right, Madgie. Don't let her bully you. You're a beast, Nan, and you know it.'

★ *Part Two* ★

At this Nancy laughed even more than ever, and her eyes seemed even greener. Marjory, feeling safe, stared across the table at her, wondering. Isa helped her to porridge and gently pushed in her chair to the table. Now she was happy. Isa's quiet manner, her gentleness, soothed her injured feelings. She smiled up at her with perfect trust. Nancy forgot her, and allowed her to eat her porridge in peace, while she talked to Willie and Isa about their plans for the day. The talk flowed over her head, but she heard every word and afterwards remembered it. Flung into the midst of this family of grown-up cousins, who alternately tormented and petted her, she was perfectly happy. Among the younger members, at least, it was a rule not to talk down to her; they expected her to stretch up to their level, or go without, and, when she failed, there was a chorus of 'Stupid girl! Why, Madgie, you're only a baby after all.' In time, if she had not properly understood the conversation, she learned not to break in on it and this was good for her. Her cousins, though more ruthless because they were young themselves, were less likely to make allowances for her and taught her more than her elders could have done. She had that kind of nature. If she could not look up to people she dominated them. She preferred to look upwards, all her life.

At the end of breakfast, Marjory folded her hands and said grace. It was a new grace and she stumbled in the middle. When she did this, Nancy raised her eyes to heaven, and heaved a pious sigh, but all she said at the end was:

'Wipe your mouth, child, it's all over milk,' before she rustled away to feed her canaries. Marjory looked shocked.

'I want to come with you, Nan,' she pleaded. 'Oh, Isa, pray let me go. I want to see the birds fed.'

'Take Madgie with you, Nan,' Isa called after her sister. 'I have to go upstairs to Mamma.'

'Come then,' said Nancy impatiently, holding open the big swing door into the kitchen passage. 'But you're to be quick, and not ask questions. I'm in a hurry.'

Marjory obediently hurried as much as she could, and was told not to dance about like a mad thing. Cousin Nancy was very hard to please. The passage was a stone one, and their voices echoed strangely in it. They got seed from the store-room for the canaries and the two green linnets. Three canaries belonged to Isa, and Marjory loved them best, although she tried not to have favourites. The cook gave them a saucer of raw meat for the hawk, which lived on a post in the passage outside the schoolroom. It belonged to Willie, and was certainly very tame, for it would sit on his wrist, and even on his shoulder, although if the monkey came near it would look very fierce. Pug knew better than to come *too* close, and when Marjory carried him past he would hide his head on her shoulder and make a great show of being afraid. Marjory herself was not at all afraid of the hawk, though he had a cruel curved beak. The post was rather high, so Nancy lifted the bird down and let the child feed it with pieces of meat. All the same, she preferred the two white cages of canaries that hung in the schoolroom windows; they were so pretty and tame, and she liked changing the water in their little white drinking-cups.

Sometimes Nancy let Marjory give them a bath, but not to-day. Up in Nana's room there was a thrush in a wicker cage, and Marjory brought worms in for it when she had been playing in the back green.

As soon as the birds were fed, she went in to say good morning to her aunt, who never came down to breakfast, and then Isa called her into the schoolroom. To-day she did not feel at a like writing, and came unwillingly. Isa was already at the table; she looked very slender in a new dress of some blue stuff, with a silver line threaded through it. Marjory climbed slowly on to her chair and opened the detestable little grey book. It did not look more attractive when half filled with her own scratchy, blotched attempts to write 'A tile in time saves nine.'

'Why cannot they make something interesting to copy?' she demanded, so woefully that Isa did not check her. Instead, she said gently:

'A great many things are not interesting or nice, Madgie, but we must have patience and perseverance.' Marjory stared and pushed out her lip.

'Why?' she asked. Isa sighed.

'Because patience is a good thing; it is a virtue and we should try to have it,' she said, although she certainly did not lack it herself. 'Writing is one thing over which we can learn to be patient—and teaching a tiresome little girl is another,' she added, with sudden asperity.

Marjory stared and dropped the pen she had rather crossly snatched from the table. She looked horrified.

Why, perhaps Isa would rather be doing a great many other things! She had not thought of it before. For a moment she paused, then flinging down the pen she climbed off her chair and ran anxiously to Isa.

'I will try to do it,' she said very earnestly. 'Only pray do not forsake me, or I am lost!'

Isa laughed, but she was touched.

'Come, then Madgie—do not get so excited,' she said, pushing her gently away. 'You *feel* things too much.'

She waited until the child was safely back on her chair, and ready to listen, then she said quite calmly:

'I quite agree that your copy-book is dull, though it has a good style. Still, there is no reason why you should not be entertained while you write. If you like the idea, I shall give you a plain exercise book and you can fill it up with what you choose. Copy it from a book, if you wish, or write what comes into your head. You may do just as you please.'

Marjory responded, as she always did, to the quiet, sensible way her cousin spoke to her. She sat up very straight, with knitted brows and considered it. It was quite a new idea.

'Anything I like?' she asked.

'Anything,' said Isa firmly. She got up, and crossed the room to the big bureau where she and Nancy wrote all their letters. In the glass-doored bookcase over it she kept Marjory's lesson books, and a pile of new exercise books. She took out a fresh one, neatly ruled with double lines, and held it out.

'Here. See, it is quite ready,' she said. 'You can begin to write in it now, for an hour. I have to go downstairs to see to one or two things. But remember, Madgie,' she added, as a

rarest good frenship books all these
dwell here but I am not sure of ease
and alternate labour useful life
Flowan Isas bed to lie

such a joy & luxury
the bottom of the bed I sleep
And with great care I myself keep
Ye I embrace her feet of lillys
But she has gotten all the pillies
Her neck I never can embrace
But I do hug her feet in place
But I am sure I am contented
And if my follies are repented

Facsimile of a poem by Marjory Fleming
In the possession of the National Library of Scotland

warning. 'It is not to be a private journal. You must let me see it. I tell you this, so you will not put anything in it you do not wish me to see.' She laughed. 'Put in it that I am a disagreeable dragon, if you wish, and I shan't mind! You are quite at liberty to tell the truth, if you think it.'

Marjory's round eyes and scandalized expression were all she needed to guess that her reputation was for ever safe in her small cousin's hands. She went away, laughing, and Marjory was left gazing at the blank page of her first journal. Not for long. A moment later she was well away, firmly clutching the pen, which spluttered and scratched cheerfully along Isa's carefully ruled lines. The room was very still. Only the clock ticked, and the canaries chirped and hopped in their cages. Occasionally a carriage rumbled by in the street outside. The child sat still too, lost in a deep concentration that no one, save Isa perhaps, had known existed. Her hand moved the pen fiercely, with effort, for it would make squiggles and blots that she never intended, her tongue stuck out with determination, as she scratched away. She was rapt. There was a look of satisfaction on her face, and now, for ever afterwards, she would pick up a pen when her thoughts struggled for expression. Isa had done more than she guessed. When she came back into the room an hour later, she found Marjory still busily writing. She yielded the book to Isa, with a sigh, watching her cousin anxiously as she began to correct it. If Isa was slightly surprised, and a little bewildered, as she read, she made no sign. Only her eyes danced. She saw, suddenly, what she had done. No child speaks easily; in the midst of the greatest joys or sorrows, he is inarticulate. Marjory's ideas and thoughts had remained hidden inside herself till Isa offered her a pen, and found her key. It was quite an event, the first page she had composed herself. It began with a vague suggestion of her copy-book, and suddenly, in a plunge, became pure Marjory.

'We should not be happy at the death of our fellow creatures, for they love life like us love your neighbour and he will love you. Bountifullness and Mercifulness are always rewarded. Isabella has admirable patience in teaching me music and

resignation in perfection. In my travels I met with a handsome
lad named Charles Balfour Esqe and from him I got ofers of
marage offers of marage did I say? Nay plainly loved me.
Goodness does not belong to the wicked but badness dishonour
befals wickedness but not virtue perciverance overcomes almost
all difficulties no I am rong in saying almost I should say always
as it is so perciverance is a virtue my Coosin says patience is a
cristain virtue, which is true. fortitude is of use in time of distress & indeed it is always of use, many people have supped in
mesery & had not had fortitude & courage to suppress there . . .

'Can I go out?' demanded Marjory, who having got nearly
everything off her chest for one morning, was not much interested in Isa's corrections. She climbed down off her chair and
poked her fingers through the bars of the cage so that the
canaries could peck it. 'Come back here and attend,' said Isa
severely. Marjory hopped back to the table on one foot. She
heaved a sigh and stood with resignation while Isabella explained her mistakes. Then the book was shut up, and put in
the table drawer.

'It is there if you should want it, at any time,' said Isa, who
had decided not to confine it to lessons. 'Now run away, and
ask Nana to get you ready to go out. I'll take you over to the
gardens myself, if you're quick.'

Marjory ran off, delighted and determined to be as quick as
possible, though she had a battle with Willie on the stairs, for
he *would* block the way, and not let her by. 'Don't rush past
your elders in that way, my child,' he admonished her, but
Marjory, enraged, pushed past him with all her might and
scampered away up the stairs with scarlet cheeks, leaving him
laughing at her.

The gardens in Charlotte Square were the meeting place of
the neighbourhood. From half-past eleven onwards, the children were turned out to play there, unless it was raining. They
were taken across the road by a nurse or a governess, or an un-
willing elder sister, and left until called in for lunch. Isa took
Marjory, and she felt very proud. Everyone must see how

beautiful her cousin was. According to custom, Isa left her at the gate. She kissed her, and said:

'Don't sit down anywhere, Madgie, it's too cold. Run about and keep warm. I'll send someone for you later on.'

Marjory nodded. Once inside, she was claimed by her own set. Sets were as rigorously observed here as in the grandest drawing-room. At first, this had puzzled her, for at home she had played with her sister and the children next door and thought no more about it. Here in Edinburgh it was very different. She was expected to play with the children whose parents visited her aunt, a system she hated at once, for Marjory was cheerful by nature and disposed to like everyone in general. Also, her contrary nature made her turn to the other children for preference. Her own set thought Marjory odd, with her downright and forceful manners, and her passionate enthusiasms. It was not good manners, Miss Green told her, to get so excited about things. Miss Green was quiet, and exceedingly genteel. She was an only child. She never wanted to play at anything, but only to walk up and down and discuss dresses. Marjory was bored, but the other children did not seem to mind. They preferred it to Marjory's games, which required a vivid imagination and a great deal of dramatic action, although they liked her to tell them stories. That would be all right in summer, but to-day it was cold. She felt like racing up and down the lawn screaming, as she certainly would have done at home.

'It is not the right kind of weather for stories,' she said, impatiently shaking off Miss Grantley, who was trying to hold her hand. Miss Grantley was always like that. She had a clinging disposition. She had been to tea with Marjory twice, and Willie and Nancy had at once christened her 'White Rabbit'. Marjory was sorry for Miss Grantley, and always tried to be nice to her, especially as Miss Green snubbed her every time she opened her mouth. Marjory hated Miss Green. Nothing, she declared, in spite of their protestations, would make her tell a story to-day. She wanted action.

'You can't think of any, that's why,' said a clear, scornful

voice behind her. Marjory turned, and saw the latest new-
comer to the Square. She had come to tea only last Thursday,
with her mother, who looked exhausted and no wonder. The
Purves family consisted of four boys and this girl Eliza. Eliza
had red hair, a snub nose, and a loud voice. She was rough, and
knocked the other children down. They hated her. Marjory, on
the contrary, was interested. She suddenly had an idea.

'Yes I can,' she said. 'I know lots. Only I'm cold. You race
me round the garden twice, and I'll tell you.'

'All right,' said Eliza and started. Followed by protesting
shrieks from poor Miss Grantley, and scornful shrugs from
Miss Green, they tore round and round the patch of green. They
danced in the puddles, and screamed, and tugged each other's
dresses. They grew warm and pink-cheeked, and untidy. Miss
Green and Miss Grantley, watching decorously from the distance, remained sedate and shivered with the cold. The disapproval made them almost friendly.

Marjory was enjoying herself for the first time since she had
been introduced to the garden. She told Eliza a story, and
Eliza promised to teach her a song. At half-past twelve pre-
cisely, the garden gate screeched on its hinges and Nancy came
to fetch her. Marjory was sorry.

'I don't want to go, Nancy,' she protested, eager to show
Eliza that she was not the only one bold enough to flout
authority.

Nancy was not impressed.

'I don't care. You're coming and that's that,' she said
sharply. 'If you think I'm standing about in a mud patch for
you, you're mistaken.'

Marjory sighed and followed her quickly, so that Eliza
should not hear any more of the way Nancy ordered her about.
It was most provoking. Once outside in the street, Nancy stared
her up and down.

'Well, you look a perfect fright, I must say,' she frankly
remarked. 'And you've torn your dress again.' She shrugged
her shoulders. 'However, that's Isa's job, not mine, thank
heavens.'

64

She pushed Marjory into the house and shut the door.

Lunch-time to-day was even worse. There were no visitors and Nancy, her green eyes alight with mischief, leaned over the table to tell Willie how she had found Madgie dancing in the Square with Eliza Purves, and shouting at the top of her voice. Marjory grew scarlet with mortification. James was at home, and what would he think of her? Marianne, seeing the child's stricken face, frowned at her daughter.

'Come, Nancy, that's enough,' she said, and Isa whispered to Marjory, 'Would you like to run off and play, Muff? I'll come presently.'

Marjory nodded. She gobbled her grace, slid off her chair, and without looking at Nancy, began to fold her table napkin. This was difficult; the creases were there, but it would not fold up neatly. She struggled in silence until Nancy, of all people, put out her hand and flicked the napkin into place. She rolled it up and put it into the ring. Marjory gave her a look of swift, uncertain gratitude. She never could quite believe it when Nancy was so kind.

By two o'clock they were all assembled in the drawing-room, looking as if it had happened by accident and not simply because visitors were expected. The drawing-room at North Charlotte Street was very beautiful. It had green and silver brocade curtains and cabinets of cut glass that tinkled when Willie crossed the room, but not when Marjory did though she stamped with all her might. Isabella was dressed in black velvet, with a fichu of lace; her skin was very white, and her eyes nearly sapphire-blue in the light. Marjory thought her a great beauty. The first to arrive was Charles Balfour, and his brother John, who was married. He had greatly shocked Marjory at their first encounter by asking her to give him a kiss, although, as she scratched very firmly into her journal 'The man was espused and his wife was present and said her must ask her permission but he did not, I think he was ashamed or confounded before 3 gentlemen Mr. Jobson and two Mr. Kings.' However, Marjory had recovered from this episode now, and she liked both the Balfours very much, but especially

Charles. He had not forgotten about being her friend, but had actually called for her one day, and taken her to see a menagerie. Marjory, who had never had such a treat before, was enchanted. She talked about nothing else for weeks, until Nancy begged Charles to leave her there, if he took her again. Marjory was indignant.

'I can't think how I ever called Willie a tease,' she confided. 'For no-one could be worse than Nancy. She is a great trial.'

Mr. Balfour looked across the room at Nancy as if he did not think so at all. One might suppose he enjoyed being teased himself, for presently he moved away, and went to stand beside her. A moment later they were deep in conversation and Marjory was alone. She felt a little dispirited, for there was nothing else to do but make conversation, and she could not do that by herself. The only person not speaking, but sitting silent and alone, as she was, was her cousin James. Marjory did not dare disturb him, so she went off by herself into one of the window seats and sat there very still, remembering to be careful of her dress.

At exactly the same moment, or so it seemed, the gilt clock on the mantelpiece chimed, the servant carried in the silver coffee tray, and Miss Potune came bustling up the stairs, laughing brightly from a great way off. Miss Potune was always laughing, mostly at her own jokes. She was very fat and rich, and lived by herself in a large house with nine red urns supported by Muses, in the garden. She was devoted to animals and children, classing them together in one fat, jovial breath, and she was sure they loved her too. Marjory hated her. She went stiff and cold the moment Miss Potune spoke to her. The very first time they had met she had been persuaded to recite, and Miss Potune had patted her on the head and talked nonsense. She wore the most vivid dresses, of scarlet and heliotrope and a gaudy bonnet with a great many floating ribbons and flowers on it. Besides all this, she had several huge and heavy necklaces of carved ivory beads that clinked and gleamed when she laughed. Worst of all, she came to tea every time she was asked. This time, luckily, she was almost immediately followed by a tall thin lady with a long aristocratic nose, and the finest little girl Marjory had ever seen. They came floating upstairs, in the wake of Miss Potune, looking rather bewildered.

The little girl, who was perhaps a few years older than Marjory, was like a china doll. She had long golden ringlets, with starry blue eyes, and she was dressed exactly like a grown-up person in miniature. Her bonnet was trimmed with fur. She said that her name was Jeanetta, and she did not pull away, but smiled angelically, when Miss Potune flung wide her arms and embraced her. Being kissed by Miss Potune, as Marjory knew, was like being flung into the centre of a huge feather bed. Her stays creaked and groaned with the exertion. It hardly seemed worth the effort, but she always did it. She looked round now for Marjory.

'Where is my dear little friend Miss Madgie?' she exclaimed and added, turning to Marianne. 'We are *such* good friends you know! I love young people. They come and tell me all their little secrets.'

'Indeed?' said the thin lady, politely. Her name was nearly as long as her nose, for it was Mrs. Bellew-Sanderson.

'Yes, indeed, the little dears!' went on Miss Potune enthusiastically. 'I suppose it is because I've kept so young myself. I'm young in heart and spirit, as I always say. Children realize that at once, of course.'

'Of course,' said the thin lady gloomily, straightening Jeanetta's dress, which had been severely crumpled between two of the ivory necklaces.

Marjory came unwillingly out from her corner. She stood as stiff as a ramrod while Miss Potune kissed her, and exclaimed how much she had grown. It happened every time she came, so she supposed she could stand it once more. She never said a word on her own. Mute, contemptuous, she stood waiting until it was over, and then she turned to Jeanetta.

'Would you like to play something?' she asked politely.

'Yes, please,' said Jeanetta, and added as an afterthought, 'If it won't spoil my dress.'

67

'Well, what would you like to do?'

Jeanetta had no idea. She stood silent. So did Marjory.

'You choose,' she urged; after all, Jeanetta was the guest; she ought to say. Nothing happened. Marjory, impatient, burst out: 'Well, what do you *know*?'

Jeanetta stood, her head bent. She whispered:

'Anything.'

Marjory sighed.

'I'll fetch our monkey. He's very funny,' she suggested, and a flicker of interest passed across Jeanetta's face.

'Yes, please,' she said.

The monkey was in a teasing mood. He sprang round the room before Marjory could capture him. She held him in her arms and whispered: 'You've *got* to be good. We've got visitors,' as she carried him back with her. Jeanetta looked amazed and a little frightened, as if she had never seen a monkey before. When Marjory asked her if she had any pets at home, she whispered, no, and came a step nearer. She put out her hand. Pug chose this moment to leap from Marjory's arms and spring on to the child's shoulder. Jeanetta, with a wail as shrill as a steam-whistle, turned, and fled. She flew to her mother and burst into tears. Marjory was shocked, and a little hurt for Pug. She did not like him to be slighted.

'Jeanetta is not very used to animals. We have none at home,' said Mrs. Bellews-Sanderson, and added rather anxiously, 'He is . . . er . . . quite *clean*, I hope?'

'Dear me! The poor little dear is afraid!' said Miss Potune unnecessarily. 'Never mind.' She clucked her tongue sympathetically. 'Suppose we have a little recital. I know dear Madgie will like to say one of her pretty pieces for us.'

'No, I won't,' said Marjory, still clutching the injured Pug. She had never known a day go so wrong in all her life. She almost hated Jeanetta, who was bawling and fussing like a child of two, and all for nothing.

'Marjory, dear,' said Marianne reproachfully. 'That's not polite, when you know so many verses. Choose one that you think Jeanetta would like.'

68

Marjory gazed desperately round. How *could* she explain? Even Isa was looking sadly at her. She knew that fat Miss Potune, Jeanetta, none of them, would care what she said. They would not even know what it meant. She pressed her lips firmly together and looked plain and cross.

'I won't,' she said.

Mrs. Bellew-Sanderson came to life. Leaning forward eagerly, she said:

'Jeanetta knows some pretty songs, don't you, my love?'

The child stopped crying, and nodded. Miss Potune clapped her hands and said it was all splendid, before she had even heard the song. Isa opened the piano, and offered to play the accompaniment. They all said something. Only Marjory stood still, her heart thumping. There was Jeanetta, smiling now, set up on a footstool in the midst of them, while everyone applauded. She looked charming in her white dress, and sang well. It was obvious that now she was completely happy. Marjory turned away her head. The injustice of it made her feel she would like to give up all pretence of being well mannered, fling herself on the floor and scream and scream.

The song ended. Jeanetta bobbed a curtsey, and stood nodding prettily at the applause, like a china doll strung on wires. Before she had time to start up again, James came forward into the centre of the room. Glancing over his shoulder at Marjory, he said with authority:

'Madgie, go and dance.'

It was so unexpected, especially from James who obstinately ignored her, that she was quite perplexed. Her mouth opened a little 'to catch sunbeams' as Isa said, and she stood still, wondering. Then Isa smiled, and began to play a jig that Marjory loved. She could not resist it. It was not breaking her word, for she had not recited. In a minute she had run out into the circle of her admiring audience, and was hopping from one foot to another like a small, wind-tossed white flower. Her eyes shone, her cheeks grew pink. She could have danced all night, for in her feet twinkled the tremendous joy and pride that surged up in her. Jamie Keith had spoken to her! There are not many

69

moments like this in a lifetime, and Marjory captured hers eagerly.

It was something worth remembering, she felt. Then, in an instant, the music stopped. She tumbled to the floor in her most beautiful curtsey. Her great moment was over.

Spring 1809

Marjory was six years old on the 15th of January 1809. She felt that it marked a great change in her life, and, upon reflection, decided to be a very good girl now she was no longer a baby. This impulse frequently came upon her, and went away again nearly as suddenly. She considered it during her play-time, which she spent curled up in the schoolroom, with the Newgate Calendar. This was her latest craze. She had found it pushed at the back of the schoolroom cupboard, and had tugged it out from a pile of old lesson books scribbled with the names of Isabella, William, Nancy, and James. The Newgate Calendar had belonged to Willie. It impressed Marjory enormously, and she felt quite daring in reading it at all. Her cousins only shrugged their shoulders when they came upon her absorbed in murder, her eyes round and grave, but told her not to let her aunt see it. Marjory dutifully sat on it when Marianne came into the room. If she shivered secretly at night, and crept under the bedclothes when Isa had taken the candle away and gone downstairs, she never told anyone; and next day, in broad sunshine, felt bold enough to write almost carelessly in her Journal 'The Newgate Calendar is very Instructive Amusing, and shews us the nesesity of doing good and not evil,' though a little later she admitted that it filled her with horror and consternation. 'Sorrow,' said Marjory, 'is a thing that sadines the heart and makes one grave sad and melancoly which distreses his relations and friends.'

Isa, trailing after Marjory's swift pen with a correcting pencil, never laughed outright. She respected the mind that was struggling for expression against the immense handicaps of spelling, writing, and punctuation. Marjory needed no bidding to pull out her journal and set down just what she liked. She hated writing anything else, and a letter made her the most martyred child in the world. Nevertheless, after a long struggle, both with Isa and her own conscience, she composed a long epistle to her sister Isabella, far away in what had become only a shadow-world to her.

My dear Isa,

I now sit down on my botom to answer all your kind and beloved letters which you was so good as to write to me. This is the first time I ever wrote a letter in my life. There are a great number of Girls in the Square and they cry just like a pig when we are under the painfull necessity of putting it to Death.

Miss Potune, a lady of my acquaintance, praises me dreadfully. I repeated something out of Dean Swift and she said I was fit for the Stage, and you may think I was primmed up with majestick Pride but upon my word I felt myselfe turn a little birsay—birsay is a word which is a word that William composed which is as you may suppose a little enraged. This horid fat Simpliton says that my Aunt is beautifull which is intirely impossible for that is not her nature.

It is a wonder that sparks did not fly from the paper when Marjory set this down, her lips pressed together, her nose nearly touching the table. It was duly addressed, sealed, and sent off, to become itself a very beloved letter indeed. The composer, released, flung herself on to the couch in delight, and hugged the long-suffering Help, until he managed to wriggle free and dive under the table, shaking it mightily.

'Don't, Madgie,' said Isa, burning her fingers with the wax. It was not a day for playing in the Square; they went down to the shops in Princes Street, and saw a great crowd of people all doing the same. Marjory forgot the letter. She had not wanted to write it very much, but it was useful because Isa, as a reward, read to her after dinner. At six years old Marjory had a wide range of books from which to choose, fiction, poetry, history; Isa denied her nothing. Fortunately, there were, then, few books written specially for children, by authors who appar-

ently endowed their audience with feeble minds. Marjory's
journal, outlook, and ideas, were strengthened, and sometimes
provoked, by the books she read. If she could not understand
them word for word, she grasped the atmosphere and meaning
at once. Just as no-one spoke childishly to her in the Keith
household, so she was not given books that were childish,
either. Her mind rose to Shakespeare, Pope, Grey, Thomson,
like a silver fish leaping from a stream. She read *Macbeth* and
thought it 'a pretty composition but awful one Macbeth is so
bad and wicked but Lady Macbeth is so hardened in guilt she
does not mind her sins and faults No.' Besides this, for amuse-
ment, she read Miss Edgeworth's tales, and every kind of novel
that came into the house. They were really for Isabella and
Nancy, but, to keep Marjory quiet, they allowed her to read
them too. Sometimes, sitting up in the schoolroom round the
fire, sewing, they took it in turns to read aloud. Marjory liked
this best; she had just begun her first piece of knitting, a tremendous affair in bright red worsted on huge wooden needles.
The novels were all in the latest fashion, and very romantic.
They belonged chiefly to a series known as the Cheap Reposi-
tory, which as they only cost a penny, were not hard to obtain.
Besides this, the Keiths bought quite a number of new books;
the novels came in three volumes, and the suspense at the end
of each one was great, although the heroine was always rescued
from her dangers. As a result, Marjory developed a tremendous
interest in anything to do with love and heroines; she asked so
many questions, and became so obsessed by it, that Isa finally
forbade her to speak about it at all. Marjory, as the next best
thing, wrote about it, but remembering Isa's pencil she carefully noted the fact each time she did so, once with disapproval.
'In the love novels all the heroins are very desperate Isabella
will not allow me to speak about lovers and heroins and tiss too
refined for my taste.' Isabella sometimes spoke about them herself, but what she and Nancy whispered to each other while
they were preparing to go to bed, Marjory never knew although
she often tried to listen. She was sure it was something very
romantic.

★ *Part Two* ★

That year was a cold, slow winter. Sometimes the bitter wind and snow prevented anyone leaving the house for days on end; the snow whirled down the streets like icy dust, and you could not open your eyes. Marjory grew dull and sad; she grew naughty too, and would not touch her copy-book for several days, nor even listen while Isa read. She only wanted to rush up and down the passages and stairs, encouraging Help and the monkey to leap up and down and make a noise. It was most annoying. She did not really enjoy it very much herself, but there was nothing else to do, except pine to go for a walk. She became quite fretful as a result. Isa promised that when the weather cleared she should have a treat, and it soon became obvious that something was going to happen. Trunks appeared in the passages, cupboards were emptied, and Willie whistled more than usual, which meant he was pleased. Marjory was intrigued, and the suspense kept her good. At last she heard that the treat was a visit to the Craufurds, some great friends of the Keiths, who lived not far from Edinburgh, in a house called Braehead. It was at Cramond Bridge, near the Firth of Forth, so she would soon see the sea again; she had missed it more than anything. Marjory loved the country; it was part of her. She could have been born and bred in a city all her life, but as soon as she stepped into a green field, she would have been lost for ever.

On the morning of their departure, she woke early. It seemed silly to waste a moment of the day, and she could not lie still. She tumbled out of bed and tiptoed into Isa's room, avoiding the cold floorboards. Isa was still asleep. Marjory stood still, watching. In sleep, her cousin seemed strange, and even more wonderful to her. She seemed to have wandered far away; her lashes lay dark against her cheek, and her face was calm. Marjory hesitated, before creeping silently away; in that moment Isa opened her eyes, looked at her, and then rolled over on the other side. She said in a muffled voice: 'Get under the cover, Madgie, and keep still,' then fell asleep again.

Marjory obediently climbed up on to the bed and settled herself at the foot, wrapped in the quilt. She kept still for five

74

minutes. The room was gradually growing lighter, and now all
the shapes of the furniture could be clearly seen. She felt so
pleased she began to wriggle her toes up and down under the
cover. Isa woke up. She said, 'Oh, *Madgie*,' and fell asleep
again. She seemed to be very sleepy. Suddenly Marjory knew
what she wanted to do. She climbed backwards on to the floor,
dragging the quilt with her. Wrapping herself in it, she put on
some slippers and trotted off to the schoolroom, looking like a
cocoon. The canaries were chirping softly under their covers;
they did not know the day had come. Marjory let up the blinds,
and flooded the room with morning, then she went over to the
table and drew out her exercise book. Settling herself on the
chair she turned to a blank page, and wrote firmly on the top
'Ephibol on my dear love Isabella.' A moment she paused, considering this, then she bent her head and wrote:

> *Here lies sweet Isabell in bed*
> *With a nightcap on her head*
> *Her skin is soft, her face is fair*
> *And she has very pretty hair*
> *She and I in bed lies nice*
> *And undisturbed by rats and mice*
> *She is disgusted with Mr. Wurgan*
> *Though he plays upon the organ*
> *A not of ribans on her head*
> *Her cheak is tinged with conscious red*
> *Her head it rests upon a pilly*
> *And she is not so very silly*
> *Her nails are neat her teath are white*
> *Her eyes are very very bright*
> *In a conspicuous town she lives*
> *And to the poor her money gives*
> *Here ends sweet Isabellas story*
> *And may it be much to her glory.*

The drive out to Braehead took several hours, but Marjory,
sitting between Isa and Willie, was too absorbed in looking out
of the window to care. Her cousins talked among themselves

and for once she hardly listened. People were always discussing
the war with France, and sometimes she grew tired of it,
though she liked to hear the tales Willie told of battles and
escapes. There was a moment of great excitement when some
of the French prisoners in Edinburgh castle got free, and were
at large for several days, so that many people were afraid to
leave their houses. Miss Potune hurried round to Mrs. Keith in
great dismay at the news, and though Marjory laughed at her,
she was very glad when all was over and the prisoners recaptured. Even her cousins did not speak of the war so often or so
gloomily as her aunt and uncle; Willie was even saying that
Buonaparte was a great general. Marjory, jerked back from her
own thoughts by this remark, exclaimed wide-eyed: 'But he's
an enemy!'

'What of it?' said Nancy carelessly. 'Even an enemy can
have good points, I suppose?'

Marjory was shocked at this. Surely no-one would be an
enemy unless they were wicked. She was silent again, considering. Once more she had grasped a new idea. Up till this
moment people had been either good or wicked, as they were in
books. Now, suddenly, she realized they might perhaps be
both; her world trembled to its foundations at the thought.

'Why!' she exclaimed, wide-eyed. 'Then—then even a mur-
derer might not be altogether bad.'

'That's it,' said Willie, laughing at her perplexity. 'You may
not find it in your precious Newgate calendar, all the same. It's
easier to find a man wicked all through than seek the good in
him.'

While she still struggled to comprehend it, they came in
sight of the sea. It was a grey, frozen day, and the waves were
fierce. Marjory forgot everything else when she saw it.

'How beautiful, it is,' she said, leaning forward, her lips
parted. 'It is very majestic.' Isa smiled down at her glowing
face. There were no leaves on the trees, and the sky was like a
stone, yet Marjory never forgot the wonder of her first sight of
Braehead. It was to become the place dearest to her heart. She
did not see it first in summer, the time she grew to know it

best, but on this cold grey February day with a high wind
blowing off the sea. Braehead looked as if it could stand up to
any storms. It was a square, high, grey house, with tall windows, and two gables built up in steps. The garden was not
very large, and contained, besides the wintry flower beds, four
yew trees and some box clipped into pretty shapes. Margaret
and Isabella came out on the steps to meet them, exclaiming at
the cold. They made much fuss of Marjory. Isabella, the
youngest, was little and gay; she had two bunches of shiny
dark curls tied up with red velvet ribbons that danced when she
moved her head. Isa and Nancy exchanged glances; they knew
perfectly well that William admired her. He had done so ever
since childhood. As to Isabella herself, it was hard to say. She
was always very gay, but somehow contrived to be never alone
with him, nor to sit next him at meals. Only, when he was not
looking, she gazed at him steadily, even sternly, with all the
mockery gone from her eyes. Marjory would have found this
very romantic if she had known; fortunately for William and
Isabella, it passed her by, until the day Isa came and told her
they were to be married. She was so used to the idea of desperate lovers and pining, wan heroines, laughing Isabella did not
wake a suspicion in her active mind. She liked Isabella at once,
although it was Margaret who paid her more attention, and
kindly gave her a little book with an inscription in it. 'All
Isabellas are nice people,' she declared, hugging her own Isa,
who was, in her eyes, more perfect and lovely than even the
wildest heroine.

Life at Braehead was leisurely and charming. It did not
matter that outside the wind blew, and the heavy sky threatened snow or rain. Marjory did not mind being shut up here as
she did in town. For one thing, she thought the swaying, leafless trees 'a noble sight', and spent quite a lot of time kneeling
on the window-seat watching them. There was also much to be
seen in the house itself. The drawing-room and dining-room
were panelled, and the walls hung with pictures of past Craufurds in satin stomachers, which fired Marjory's imagination,
and pleased her. She loved the leaping fires in the wide hearths

which scented all the house with pine. It was mixed with lavender, from the tall china jars of pot-pourri that stood on chests in the passages. Every day, she learnt her lessons with Isa, as she did at home. Mrs. Craufurd was away at the time on a visit, and they were allowed to use her sitting-room for a schoolroom. Marjory was not permitted to touch anything. She sat up on a high chair with a carved back to do her lessons, or on a dear little tapestry footstool while Isa read aloud to her. At this time, she learned a new poem. It became the loveliest thing in her life, part of Braehead the beautiful, and the quiet, firelit room where she sat, her small rebellions quenched into a sudden, passive happiness. 'The delight of my soul,' said Marjory one day, her clear look taking in the whole room, and Isa laughing at her across the table. 'I wish we could live here always.' That was impossible; but the poem was lovely, and she could have *that* for always. It was 'Helvellyn' a rather sentimental ballad about the fate of a young man who lost his way on the great mountain, and died. His remains were discovered three months afterwards, still faithfully guarded by his little terrier bitch. Marjory thought this extremely mournful and beautiful. She had the good taste to pick out the best verse for her favourite, instinctively, and begged Isa to read it again and again. For the moment it thrilled her every time she heard it, and she never had time to out-grow it.

Lessons ended with 'Helvellyn' these days. Isa shut the book, and Marjory slid off her chair, nearly bumping her nose on the table in her eagerness to be away. At home she lingered behind, making every excuse to avoid going into the Square. Here, there was so much to do, and to see, she was busy every moment of the day. Humming to herself, her eyes shining, she piled up the lesson books on the table until to-morrow. Isa watched her curiously. Marjory's state of mind had a tremendous effect on her body. In a few days she had grown sturdy and plump, and quite unlike the white, cross child in Edinburgh.

'Well, and where are you going in such a hurry?' she asked at last.

Watercolour of Braehead House

Marjory stopped. She shrugged her shoulders.

'Out,' she said vaguely, waving her hand at the window. She came to stand beside Isa for a minute, coaxing for a kiss. As soon as it was given she was out of the room and down the stairs like a flash. Presently the gate in the courtyard creaked open, and Marjory ran out into the fields carrying a biscuit in one hand and a very small basket in the other. She was off to find the eggs, which was her own special job. It was lovely to look for the stray ones under the hedges, and in the orchard's tangled grass below the apple-trees, where the hens strutted and pecked. They were more tidy about their laying in the winter, and kept to the shelter of the hen-house. Marjory put her hand right under the fat, brown hen and took out the egg. There was no ill-feeling on either side. She loved the feel of the egg, warm and smooth and *living*, in her hand. She held it very carefully and always, gravely, she bobbed a little curtsey and said 'Thank you' to the hen, who blinked disdainfully with its beady little eyes. Of course, she never did this if Biddy, the kitchen girl, was with her, or Nancy, or either of the Miss Craufurds. It was just something she did when she was alone. The brown eggs were the prettiest, and the best in every way. Somehow, there were never quite so many of them as the plain white ones. Marjory had been told many times that the colour of the hen had nothing at all to do with the egg it laid, but she never quite believed it, and always crept up to the large brown hen *hoping* the egg would be brown too. She always kept the first brown egg for Isa. One day, at breakfast, Nancy had taken it instead, and Marjory had made a disgraceful scene. She had flung down her spoon and bawled like a child of two, and everyone had been shocked. No-one really understood how much it meant to her, that Isa should have the brown egg. She sometimes found a special one for Willie too, a big one; or for Mr. George Craigie if he happened to have ridden over to breakfast. This young man was as cheerful as his name, and a great friend of Marjory's. He was very amusing and gay, and knew a great many stories. He lived at Craigie Hall, a neighbouring house, and there was much visiting between his family and Braehead, for there were always parties of young people there. Marjory liked company, and she was not left out. If anything, she preferred to be with her cousins and their friends to children of her own age, or else by herself. Writing once in her journal, she proclaimed, 'I like loud merriment and laughter,' but added almost at once, 'I love to walk in lonely solitude' which was just as well, for there were not many children living near by. The next-door estate was Dalmeny, owned by Lord Rosebery, and the Craufurds did not visit there. He was rather a strange person, who also liked to be left alone, and Marjory gleaned most of her information about their neighbour from Biddy. The walk to Craigie Hall lay through Dalmeny woods, or she would not have been interested. When she heard he had tried to break up a rookery by shooting the rooks, her indignation was very great, and she spent a wet afternoon composing an imaginary letter to rebuke him. Otherwise, the Miss Craufurds kindly invited Miss Bonner, the local parson's little girl, to come and play with Marjory. She was a quiet, meek little girl, and Marjory took entire charge from the moment they met and as usual, was unopposed.

When she had carefully collected the eggs in her basket, and hung it up on a nail by the kitchen door, she ran off into the words. Braehead stood at the head of a deep glen, and the woods wound down to the river far below. Marjory sometimes walked down to the village with Isa, and they paused to lean on the old bridge and watch the brown water swirl away beneath it. If you stood long enough, staring at a buttress jutting out into the water, you could really believe you were in a moving ship. Marjory believed it, anyway. Sometimes, she would be taken to the mill and shown the big water-wheel churning round. This was a treat belonging to the Craufurds' childhood, and they thought it would please Marjory too. Actually, she hated the water-wheel. She stood just inside, as near to the door as she could keep, and watched it with round eyes, quaking inwardly. Nothing would have induced her to admit that the crashing, tumbling wheel filled her with such horror, especially as meek little Miss Bonner did not mind it at all. On the contrary, it was one of the few times she became animated. She laughed and screamed, and tore up handfuls of grass to throw into it. Marjory watched, awed.

Besides the big river that flowed under the bridge, a burn trickled down through the woods. It was Marjory's favourite play-place when she was alone. She stayed by it for hours, floating leaves and sticks in it, damming it up and letting it gush forth again in a waterfall, and even tumbling into it. In winter the water was icy cold, and ran with a sharp sound like icicles tinkling, but she loved it just as much. The red winter sun as it sank, streamed through the leafless trees, and the child ran up and down, utterly absorbed in her game.

A courier came from Edinburgh in the late afternoon. It meant nothing to Marjory, but Isa, who was expecting a letter, ran down to meet it. There was one for her, and it brought the news she had wanted. She carried it up to the schoolroom, where she had been correcting one of Marjory's lessons, and settled down eagerly to read it. Early that year, some friends had proposed a visit to Melrose Abbey, and invited her to join them. It had not been possible to make plans then, but now everything was settled for the spring. Isa, in her delight, remembered Marjory. When the child came, she had faithfully promised her mother that she would look after her properly, and not grow tired, or shirk her task half-way through. She had done so, giving up many pleasures and excursions and visits to friends to make sure Marjory had her lessons. It was the first time she had gone away, but now the child was no longer strange she did not feel wrong about it. Nancy had promised to look after Marjory, and be gentle with her—for Isa, fussing like the mother of six children, was worried by her sister's sharp ways. They would return home to North Charlotte Street before the visit was over, and then her mother had promised to continue the lessons herself. Isa felt perfectly satisfied. She stood by the schoolroom window, drumming her fingers on the pane, and wondering what she should take. She had a new black velvet for the evening, with a white lace shawl. Isa, who had never had a black velvet before, felt very old, and responsible; to be sure, she was now eighteen. Suddenly she thought, 'I must tell Madgie I am going. If I tell her now, she won't mind so much.' She turned from the window, fetched her cloak, and went out into the wintry garden.

Marjory, stirring up a great puddle with a long stick, saw Isa's scarlet cloak coming up through the trees. She carefully put the stick into a hollow tree where she kept it, because she was not allowed to bring such things into the house, and came running down to meet her. She jumped on a tree-stump and held out her hand. 'Come up here, and I'll let you be King of the Castle,' she said. 'I'll let you do anything, if you will play with me!'

'I haven't come out to play with you,' said Isa laughing. 'I've come to ask you a question.'

Marjory looked solemn. She came and put both her hands into Isa's and gazed earnestly up at her.

'Ask me,' she said.

'I want your advice, Muff,' said Isabella slowly, using her own pet name for her cousin.

She took the child's hand and they went up the path together, into the full rays of the sun, sinking in a last burst of glory. It lit Isabella's face, and turned her hair to gold.

'You see,' she said, in her quiet, calm voice, while Marjory walked beside her taking in every word. 'You see, I brought you here, Muffy, because you needed a change. Everyone does, at the end of a long winter—not only a change of scene, but a change of occupation too. You see how gay and well you have become at dear Braehead, among the woods! But I have a chance now too, of a great change. To go on a visit for a few weeks to Melrose Abbey with some very kind friends who want me to join them. I should like to go, and to be free of lessons for a little while, just like you, but first of all I want to ask you what you think. If you think you will be a good girl until I come back, and be obedient to Nancy, who will take care of you, and not fret, then I will go, and have a happy time, because I can trust you. But if you feel you will be naughty and passionate, and not try to be a good girl, then I shall not go, because it would make me so very ashamed. Which do you think it will be?'

There was a great silence. The shadows of the trees crept up to where Isa stood, holding Marjory's hand, and waiting to know what she would say. The child stood silent, a little lost before the great change that suddenly threatened her. Not to have Isa for several weeks! Her cheeks grew pink; she breathed very hard and gripped Isa's hand tightly. A tremendous struggle passed over her. She knew that Isa must go, that it was fair she should have a holiday, but she was too honest to pretend she liked it. The wood, now growing cold and dark, the burst of crimson where the sun had dropped behind the trees, Isa's dear and lovely face, dimmed suddenly in a mist of tears. Isabella did not hurry her. She began to walk slowly on again, still holding Marjory's hand, her eyes were very wise and kind. All at once, without warning, Marjory stopped. They had reached the edge of the wood, where it joined the garden. Struggling with her sobs, she said in a very small, correct voice: 'I—I think you will be very much pleased with Melrose Abbey, Isa, for from what I hear it is a very fine old building indeed!'

Isabella bent, and kissed the top of her head.

'Thank you, Muff,' she said. They walked together in silence up to the house.

Nothing more was said that evening, and Marjory, having made a tremendous and victorious effort to compose herself, was more than usually gay. Isa could not go until the spring, anyway, and though the weather was fine, there was still ice on the water in the morning. A party drove over from Craigie Hall, and she was allowed to stay up past her bedtime to hear them all play and sing, and William danced with Isabella Craufurd, and Georgie with Isa. Marjory liked him so very much, she felt quite sad because of her old friend, Mr. Balfour. Her aunt had written to say that both the Mr. Balfours were going away for a long time, perhaps for ever; they had sent messages to Isa and Nancy, and to Marjory also. Overcome, she had cried, 'But I will never forget them, never, never!' and she never did; but they were gone, and Mr. Craigie was here, and very amusing. When Isa came to call her to bed, he insisted on having just one dance with her, and she was delighted. Isabella was glad too, because it sent her to bed with pink cheeks and shining eyes.

When they had taken the candle away, and left her alone in the shadowy room, a great loneliness came over the world. The singing and loud merriment seemed very far away. Sitting up in the shadows, Marjory's sorrow rushed back on her with fresh intensity. Rolling over she buried her head in the pillow, and sobbed. It was terrible of Isa to leave her; she knew she could never bear it, and Nancy was disagreeable. She sobbed most passionately, because she was alone and there was no longer any need to keep up appearances. Isa, coming upstairs when the guests had gone home to dinner, heard it, and paused with her hand on the doorknob. She wanted to go in, but she must not. Her hands clenched on the knob, she stood listening.

'She's got to learn from life,' she told herself, while pity surged up in her. 'She's got to learn to let go of people. No-one belongs to another. If I go in to her, it will make it worse. She must fight it out for herself.'

Quietly releasing the door-handle, she moved away very softly. Nothing is more desolate than a child's sorrow; you might have thought a world was breaking. Then, for no reason, the sobs grew less and less, died away altogether, and finally were changed into the even breathing of a deep and innocent sleep.

Spring had come at last. When they left Braehead the hedges were sprouting green, and the trees in the wood seemed to break into leaf every day. Even in Edinburgh, there was a new, glad feeling, the shops showed straw bonnets trimmed with buttercups and daisies instead of curling white feathers, and an old woman with a red shawl came into the Square every day with a basket of catkins, and all kinds of leaves. Marjory leaned from the schoolroom window to watch her go by, although she had meant not to get up from the table until she had finished her letters. It was so difficult, when outside the sky was blue, and the air soft and sweet with spring. It was very quiet in the house. She came back to the table, and took up her pen. If Isa were at home, she would be shocked at such lack of perseverance. Marjory shook her head. Thinking what to say was not generally a trouble with her, and she was disquieted by it. It was a very long time since her last letter home, although soon after she left her father had written himself to tell her of the new baby sister just born. They were going to call her Elizabeth. Marjory had written at once, but since then many weeks had passed, and she felt secretly guilty. Everyone should write to their parents; should *want* to write. She had written to Isa once a week since she left. It was this knowledge which pricked her conscience like a little thorn. She was too honest to disregard it. Child though she was, she had a strong sense of restitution; to make up for her neglect she had deliberately shut herself in on a bright afternoon to finish the letter begun before lunch as a writing lesson. It was the bright, cheerful letter of a child writing home from a brave new world where she feels entirely happy and at ease. There was nothing in it about wanting to come back, or feeling sad. There were no longings, such as she sent to Isa, pleading for her return in the same breath as she dutifully hoped she was enjoying herself. In the months since she had left home, Marjory had grown, developed, and shed any remnants of babyhood, and become a little girl. Her letter was bright, gay, just loving enough but not confiding. She had no secrets to tell. It is to be feared she showed off a little for her sister Isy's benefit when she came to read it.

My dear Mud,

I hope you are well: give my love to Isa and baby, and I will send them something. I have been often at Ravelstone and once at Aunt Fleming and Mrs. Miller. I've been acquainted with many very genteel girls, and Janetta is a very fine one. Help is been confined another time. My sleeves is tucked up, and it was very disagreeable, my collar and I abhorred it amoniable.

I saw the most prettyist two tame pidgeons you ever saw and two very wee small kittens like our cat.

★ Part Two ★

I am very much acquainted with a young gentleman called Mordecai that I am quite in love with, another called Captain Bell, and Jamie Keith, and Willie's my great tormentor.

A good-natured girl gave me a song book, and I am very happy.

I'll go down and be thinking when I'm eating my dinner more to tell you, Mud.

Aunt has got two of the most beautifullest Turtle Doves you ever saw. They coo for everlasting and fight. The hawk is in great spirits, it is a nice beast, the gentlest animal that ever was Seen, Six canaries, two green linnets, and a Thrush.

Isa has been away for a long time and I've been wearying for her sadly. I like Isa and Nan very much.

I play in the back green, and bring in worms for the thrush.

I've done a pair of garters for Isabella but one of them is to short. I will work it larger and work some for Nancy too.

I get very long tasks and when I behave I get them short.

Orme Keir is the greatest recovery ever was, and he's thinking about business.

My aunt lets out the Birds to get the air in her room.

The young gentleman I was speaking of Mordecai, he's very funny.

James Keith hardly ever Spoke to me, he said Girl! make less noise and when there was a storm sometimes said take out away all your iron, and once before he said Madgie, go and dance, which I was very proud of.

Mind my Dear Mud, to return this letter when you return Isabella's.

I've forgot to say, but I've four lovers, the other one is Harry Watson, a very delightful boy.

Help is very like a tiger when he bites his fleas, a fine, gentle, wise creetyur.

Willie was at the Moors, but he soon came back again, for the Moors was like a fish pond like Miss Whyts.

I've slept with Isabella but she cannot sleep with me. I'm so very restless. I danced over her legs in the morning and she cried Oh dear you mad Girl, Madgie, for she was sleepy.

The whole house plagues me about 'Come haste to the wedding' for there is no sense in it; they think, because it is an Merican, Eliza Purves taught me, they plague me about it exceeding much. I'm affronted to say it, it is so awkward.

Remember your dear Madgie.

Amen.

Finis.

M.F. Six years old.

It was very dark. They had taken the candle away, because it was dangerous, and Nancy had forgotten to order more night-lights. Marjory begged them to leave the door open. She lay in bed, attached to the waking world by that narrow ribbon of light. It shone on the legs of the big chair where her clothes lay neatly folded, ready for the morning. However often they told her, she could not believe that, in darkness, the room was exactly the same as in the light. It creaked and moved with a horrible, stealthy life of its own. If you looked closely into it, the darkness swarmed with a hundred little twisted shapes, and was never still. Marjory, her prayers said, lay down with her eyes tightly closed, and tried not to open them again until morning. To-night, she had to keep awake. She could not miss Isa, who was coming home on the late coach. She listened, leaning up on one elbow, to every sound in the quiet house. She heard Nana go down to her supper, and Nancy call up the stairs for Willie to bring down her shawl. She had a most beautiful shawl from Spain, patterned with golden flowers, and she wore it over her shoulders at meal-times, because the drawing-room was cold. Marjory admired it immensely. After this, there was a long silence. She fell into a reverie, watching the beam of light on the ceiling, like an arm. She was not quite happy about it. When the night air crept under the window curtains, and the door stirred, the beam slid rapidly over the ceiling and became at once a monstrous thing, a Pacing Arm. There were a whole family of these strange creatures living in the cracks on the ceiling. Marjory was afraid of them, but she lay very still, and watched them as they slid across the room, over her head. Presently she heard a faint scratching near the wainscot. She sat up, wide awake, her heart thumping. Oh, why didn't Isa come! Please God make her come *soon*. Something was scratching at the door, pushing it open. While she watched, horrified, a little, strange, furry head came round the corner and stared at her with two very bright, sharp eyes.

'Oh, Pug!' cried Marjory, in a whisper. Her relief was so great, she felt weak. In a second she was out of bed, and had wrapped him up in her own rough, woollen, everyday shawl that hung at the end of the bed. She climbed back again, triumphant. At least she would have company for a while. Firmly, she set him down at her feet and held up a warning finger.

'If you don't move, I'll tell you a story,' she promised and added, half pleading, '*Please* let me tell you a story.'

Pug, finding himself comfortably curled in a warm shawl, had no objection. He kept quite still, lulled by the sound of her voice. Marjory, lying flat on her back, tracing the words in the air with her finger, began to speak. The story flowed from her mind in a thin thread of sound from between her parted lips, sometimes in prose, sometimes in verse; sometimes she sang it. It scarcely seemed to brush against the encircling darkness. The beauty, the wonder of it, soothed her. The words grew slower, softer, and then ceased altogether. She slept—and the carriage stopped at the door.

'Hush—Marjory!' said Isa, remembering her. She came up the stairs very softly, and stood for a minute just inside the room, watching the sleeping child with the monkey curled at her feet. In sleep, stirring, she smiled. She lay there, softened and vanquished, only her uncertainty, her childishness, remaining. The rest was gone. Isa, sighing, gathered up Pug, and passed into her own room. It looked desolate, cold, with no silver bottles on the dressing-table, and no clothes on the chair. She sighed, slipping off her cloak. Only on the writing-table there was a little vase of flowers, and an exercise book. Marjory's journal! It lay there, flat and blotted, and as limp as the sleeping child herself. Isabella, lighting the candle, bent to look at it. She turned to the last page, and watched, with shining

88

eyes, those big, black, scrawling words marching between the lines. It was a message, left for her to read; painfully, in the only way she knew, she had scratched the words she had tried to stay awake to say:

'My address to Isabella on her return.

'Dear Isabella you are a true lover of nature thou layest down thy head like the meak mountain lamb who draws its last sob by the side of its dam taken from hill Villean a poem by Walter Scott and a most beautiful one it is indeed this address I composed myself and nobody assisted me.'

Once again, as she read, she sensed that strange power pushing up between the childish sentences, like a flower from the dark earth; and held her breath with the wonder of it. Then she closed the book, blew out the candle, and went softly to bed.

PART III

PART III

Ravelston
July 1809—April 1810

W hen summer came, the days were long and bright. The grass in the Square gardens grew limp and brown; only a few listless, left-behind children played there now. At noon, the blinds were drawn to shut out the hot sun, burning scarlet on the flowers in their neat green boxes. The rooms within became dim and cool; even the carriages rumbled by as if in a dream. From the gardens there drifted the sweet, rich scent of lilac. When Marjory sat on the shiny leather couch in the hall, she stuck to it. She waited, breathless, for her aunt to order the trunks to be brought out, and packed! In summer Braehead was like a green, secret world; the river ran swiftly down between the trees. Isabella had told her about it.

This summer, however, they were to go to Braehead for only a week at first, and then on to Ravelston. When Marjory heard this, she looked disagreeable. Ravelston was a beautiful house, the home of Isa's grandparents. When she visited there she wore her best dresses every day, and was petted a great deal. She could not say she did not enjoy herself; but she had wanted so much to spend the whole long summer at her beloved Braehead, and had quite made up her mind about it. Braehead, to be sure, was not so fine a place as Ravelstone, but everyone was always happy there. Isa, Nancy, and the Miss Craufurds laughed all the time, and with visits to Craig Hall, and day-long picnics by the sea, the days passed in a flash. Life at Ravelston was much more grand and stiff. Isabella's grandparents were old, and did not care very much for loud merri-

ment and laughter, or noises of any kind. As a result, both Isa
and Nan became very sedate. It was 'Hush, Marjory!' whenever she opened her mouth. Meal times were an ordeal; they
were very long and stately, and the silver forks and spoons
were so heavy, Marjory had to grasp them with both hands.
One day, she knocked them on to the floor with a loud clatter,
and ever since then had been given a babyish-sized spoon and
fork of her own. This made her feel very ashamed, especially
when visitors were present, which they nearly always were. She
was very glad that Mr. Craigie could not see her being so much
affronted.

They drove to Ravelston in the carriage, just as they had
done on her first visit to Braehead. Marjory sighed when she
thought of it. William did not look any more pleased than she,
for that matter. He had just become engaged to Isabella Craufurd, and had not the least desire to leave Braehead, and visit
his grandparents. Only Isabella, as usual, did not seem to
mind, not to notice that a rather sulky and unusual silence
hung over the carriage. She sat, cool and lovely in a white
dress with a lilac taffeta sash, and lilac ribbons in her bonnet,
looking out of the window. Nancy wore her favourite shade of
green, leaf-pale, which accentuated the auburn lights in her
hair, and made her eyes more greeny-glittering than ever.
William told her she looked like a witch. She did not seem to
mind, but smiled wickedly, secretly to herself, showing her
flashing white teeth. Then, in a careless, innocent voice she
remarked that she would rather marry anyone than a round-
faced chit with hair like bunches of currants, and she knew
some men who would, too. William grew very angry at this,
and the more angry he got the more cool Nancy became. At
last she said it was too hot to argue, and leaned back in the
corner, fanning herself.

'Really, Nan . . .' said Isa, but she laughed too, for William
never could be teased, even as a small boy, though he was
always teasing others. When he got angry, he looked almost
the same as he did then, because Nancy had said that he
cheated at hide-and-seek.

★ *Ravelston: July 1809—April 1810* ★

There was peace for some time after this, but presently Nancy grew bored, sat up, yawned, and looked round for something to do. She began to tease Marjory; this was not very hard. Since she came to Edinburgh, she had grown quite used to any amount of teasing, and was rather proud of it. She was allowed to answer her cousins back as much as she chose, and she soon learned how to stop them. Suddenly, in the last few weeks, she had grown very touchy. If Isa laughed at something that amused her in the journal, or while correcting a writing lesson, Marjory burst into tears of rage. Now, when Nancy laughed at her, her cheeks grew suddenly crimson; clenching her hands, she stamped her feet and shouted out 'I won't be teased! I won't! I won't!' which was not at all like herself. Isa shook her head warningly at Nancy, who seemed herself quite amazed, though she only shrugged her shoulders and said:

'Well, if she's such a little baby, I shan't speak to her at all.'

'That will be a hardship,' William told her gloomily. 'I can't think why you won't let people alone, Nan. You've got such a damned sharp tongue, that's your trouble.'

'Willie!' said Isa, frowning at him, but she added quite sharply to the sobbing and enraged Marjory: 'Stop crying, Madgie, and sit up at once. Your dress won't be fit to be seen, and we're nearly there. What do you suppose Grandmamma will say?'

Marjory hoped Grandmamma would say, 'What *is* he matter, my poor lamb!' so that she could explain about Nancy's badness without telling tales, and she continued to sniff sorrowfully for several minutes. However, as Isa only told her to use a handkerchief, she gave it up and looked out of the window instead. The park at Ravelston was very fine, and rabbits with bobbing white tails were frisking in all the fields. Marjory liked them so much she cheered up enormously. When the carriage stopped at the door she hopped out at once with a bright, smiling face, so that the first thing Grandmamma said was: 'Well, here's my cheerful little Marjory back to see us again! Will you give me a kiss, my love?' Marjory stood on

95

tip-toe to embrace her, with a shining, angelic face. You never would have thought that the moment before she had been sobbing and screaming on the carriage floor.

Ravelston was a fine modern house, designed by Adam. Visitors exclaimed about the beautifully proportioned rooms, and the carving over the mantelpieces. Marjory, sitting up on two velvet cushions, to make her the right height, listened, her mouth open wide. When Isa reminded her, she quickly popped something into it and began to chew. She was not supposed to talk at meal-times as she did at home, but she listened just as much. As a result, she was very much left behind, solemnly eating her meat when everyone else was getting a clean, new plate for pudding. She chewed and chewed while she listened, it is true, but it was always the same piece. Isa got quite impatient with her, for she wanted Marjory to be at her best on a visit. Marjory, eager to please her cousin, hastily swallowed a very large piece, and got hiccups. She had to drink some water, whereupon Grandmamma looked down the table from her seat at the far end, and said authoritatively:

'That child should take a glass of wine every day, Isa. Water is most unhealthy. I never drank it as a child. Never was allowed to.'

'Yes, ma'am,' said Isa meekly, but when her grandmother was not looking, she made a face. A small glass of wine was brought round on a silver tray, and she filled it up with water before she gave it to Marjory.

'If you don't like it, you're *not* to spit it out,' she whispered firmly.

Marjory nodded, and drank it up with a surprised expression, while Grandmamma watched.

'Like it?' she asked, and when Marjory obediently said she did, she called her a good girl and said she could run off and play, if she liked. The visitors were now discussing the dining-room, which was unique. It was completely oval, and the table round which they sat was oval too. The carpet had been specially made for the room. They did not even notice a rather plain child in a white dress, firmly saying her grace with bright pink cheeks (for she was not going to leave *that* out, even if they didn't like her to speak). In another minute she was out of the room, and tumbling down the steps into the garden, in her eagerness to be free.

Life at Ravelston soon formed itself into a pattern and became, as everything does in time, a matter of routine. Marjory had her own schoolroom, and a little bedroom next to Isabella's, which in itself should have made her perfectly contented. All the rooms were very bright and airy, with high ceilings and white walls. Her bedroom had a pale blue carpet scattered with bunches of spring flowers loosely tied with pink ribbons. It had come from France, and the chintz curtains were of the same gay pattern. On the walls there were framed samplers, sewn by Grandmamma and her children years ago. In Isa's room there were Flemish flower paintings on wood. In the schoolroom there was a delightful clock; with two little men who struck at an anvil with tiny hammers each time the hour sounded. Since there were no parties or young people to distract her, Isa was able to devote her whole time to Marjory, teaching her, and reading to her. Sometimes they went for walks in the fields, when it was cool in the evening or the early morning, and sometimes just before bedtime Willie and Nancy would join in a game of hide-and-seek in the garden. There was a very big and beautiful garden at Ravelston, with a stream running through it, and immense clipped yew hedges rising to the sky. Once there had been a very much older house which had been burned down: all that remained of it was a doorway, and part of a tower with a turret staircase in it, and a fountain built into the wall. Marjory loved to play there, for like most children, she made houses out of anything and brewed wine from currants shaken up with water in a green glass bottle. Isabella came to tea and was given raspberries to eat on green-leaf plates, and rose-petal cakes.

Marjory should have been perfectly happy, then; but she was not. All the time that her little-girl self was running happily about the garden, or doing her lessons, there was another, darker self wakening inside her. She was growing. Her mind, leaping ahead of her body, formed sensations and knowledge that, as yet, should not have come to her. She was tormented by things that no-one could guess she would feel; she never told. With the valiant, agonized secrecy of childhood, she kept it all locked inside her. She fought alone. If despairing, she cried, without knowing why, her hot, useless tears were smothered in her pillow at night. Yet, no such tremendous growth and struggle could go on entirely silently. It showed in her sudden outbursts of temper and tears, her sulkiness and brooding, which before had been quite alien to her nature. Now, she brooded darkly in corners, and cast injured looks at poor Isa. She seemed to turn even against this dearest cousin, whom she loved so deeply, with the entire force of her personality. Every child was brought up naturally to suppose that its parents came first; it was even written in the Bible 'Honour thy father and thy mother, that thy days may be long in the land.' Marjory, incapable of self-deception, faced the fact that if all her family were drowning, and Isa too, and she could save but one of them, it would be Isa. The knowledge appalled her. She grappled with it alone, and suffered. Bound with the conventions of her elders, she was sure her wickedness was quite unique. Tentatively, it is true, she once asked Nana what would happen if you loved some other friend or relation better than your mother, and would it be very wrong? 'Well, of course it would, Miss Madgie, it would be a sin,' was the answer —and yet she was a good woman. 'Every little girl loves her mother and father best. 'Tis only natural.'

She accepted this, unquestioning. Her mind could not grasp that Nana, perhaps, was not the best person to ask. She was an older person, and therefore knew. The answer had been given, Marjory was wicked.

This was a sufficiently hard burden to bear, but it was only a part of her troubles at this time. It made her naughty and tiresome, so that even Grandmamma noticed it, and recommended Senna tea. Isabella herself was in despair. Marjory did not seem to care. It was almost as if an evil spirit made her rebel against Isa, who never lost her temper. She *wanted* Isa to lose it. She wanted to make her angry. She wanted Isa to punish her. Isabella refused, and so she won. She conquered, and kept Marjory's respect, because she was stronger. The journal, reflecting her little world, became nothing but a tale of woe, and repentance, although she had been given her new one at beautiful Braehead, and had started it off quite happily there.

' I confess that I have been more like a little young devil than a creature for when Isabella went up the stairs to teach me religion and my multiplication and to be good and all my other lessons I stamped with my feet and threw my new hat which she made on the ground and was sulky, and was dreadfully passionate, but she never whipped me but gently said Marjory go into another room and think what a great crime you are committing letting your temper get the better of you but I went so sulkily that the Devil got the better of me, but she never whipes me, so that I think I would be the better of it and the next time that I behave ill I think she would do it for she never does it but she is very indulgent to me but I am very ungrateful to her.'

She wrote this out while the dreadful passion still seized her, shaking with sobs, so that she could hardly hold the pen. The strain of the turmoil, caused half by physical development, and half by mental, was nearly too much to bear. Grandmamma, hearing about this latest trouble, saw only a sullen, obstinate child, sobbing from temper. Few people know how great is a child's capacity for emotional upheaval. Marjory, raising her head as Isa closed the door and left her alone to meditate, had the twisted, miserable face of an old woman. She was six and a half years old.

Waking early, she never lay long in bed, but dressed very quickly and ran out into the garden. The big yew hedges looked lovely with the dew sparkling on the tops of them. Marjory felt quietened and at peace. She thought she would gather two or three beautiful roses, and take them to Isabella, to show her how sorry she was that she had been so naughty lately. On

Sunday in church she had stood up on her hassock and played about during the service, and would not be still until Isa had taken her out, and then she had burst out laughing so loudly that everyone had turned round. Instead of being sorry at this, she was glad, and would have done much more if there had been time. Isa had taken her by the hand, and led her outside, where she sat her firmly down on a tombstone, and talked to her very gravely. Even then, Marjory would not listen, but swung her legs to and fro, kicking the stone, which was very wrong. Afterwards, she had been sorry for Isa had been grave and quiet all day, and at night when she came to hear Marjory's prayers she had taken both her hands and said very earnestly:

'Madgie, if you are troubled or uneasy in your mind, and this makes you behave so ill, pray tell me, and I will try to help you. I only want to do what is right for you. What is the matter? You have not been yourself since we came.'

Marjory's cheeks grew very pink, but she only looked down at her hands, imprisoned in Isa's, and whispered:

'Nothing, I am quite well.'

Since then, she had tried very hard to be good, and discovered that, after all, her case was not hopeless. A little effort went a long way. She gave her whole attention to lessons, even the multiplication table, which was her greatest trial. She could remember endless verses of poetry by heart, but never nine times nine.

'It is what nature itself can't endure,' she declared, gazing at a tragic mess of scribbles and scrawls, which represent Adding and Subtracting on her slate.

To-day was Saturday, and it seemed impossible that it should not be a good day. She had only to grapple with sums in the morning, for all the afternoon was free. In addition, Isa gave her pocket money. She had a whole sixpence every week, but it did not go very far because she was fined twopence every time she bit her nails. Not that there was much to buy and Marjory did not care for toys. She made her own amusements and she loved to give. With the pennies she saved she bought little gifts to send home to her sisters, or surprises for Isa. This week she had a new scheme on foot, for yesterday she had fallen out with John, the coachman, a very great friend of hers. Running with Isa into the stable to order the carriage for Grandmamma, she had asked him to lift her up so that she might give her favourite horse a lump of sugar. John had told her to wait a bit, because he was busy. This reply did not suit Marjory at all; she stamped with both her feet and called him 'a impudent bitch' which was the worst insult she could think of just then. She had been dreadfully sorry afterwards, especially when Isa explained that this was a word which should never pass a lady's lips, and though she at once apologized, and promised never to do so again, she was not satisfied. She decided to save up her pocket money until she could buy John a present, and then it would be all right again. She wished she knew what he would like. Once, on her birthday, he had given her a pig made out of pink sugar. Marjory thought it the loveliest thing she had ever seen. Though she was not allowed to eat it, it stood on the schoolroom mantelpiece for a week, during which time she often gave it a secret lick. Luckily, it ended by being scrunched into pieces by Help, who found it on the floor, and was much mourned by Marjory. She could never hope to find a present half so beautiful as that.

She walked in the garden a long time before she found the rose. It was the most lovely flame pink, tipped with gold. 'A sunset rose' Marjory called it, for she did not know its real name. She carried it in for Isa, and laid it beside her place at breakfast.

'I want to be very good to-day,' she said, so anxiously that Willie laughed. Nancy frowned at him, and he said very quickly:

'Tell you what, Madgie, we'll go to a race next week. There's a big one coming off then, I hear. Would you like it?'

'Yes, I would,' said Marjory, who was always pleased when Willie asked her to accompany him anywhere. 'I never was at a race in my life,' she added, making it sound a very long time indeed. She was quite sure now that it was going to be a good day. When she went upstairs to do her lessons, Isa told her that soon they would be returning to Braehead, and spending the rest of the summer there. Marjory was glad. She liked Ravelston, especially the yew hedges and the glass of wine she had every day, but she had not behaved well since they came. A change of scene might help. At Braehead she would certainly be very good indeed; it was too beautiful to spoil with tempers and scenes.

Saturday morning lessons were not very serious. As a rule, Nancy and Willie were turned out of the schoolroom, because they interrupted, and made Marjory laugh. On Saturdays she generally wrote a page in her journal as a writing lesson, and Isa let them come in. She herself sat at the table with a new dress she was making for Marjory. Willie was stretched on the sofa with a book, and Nancy, leaning over Isa, helped her to pin the pattern correctly. Through the open windows the sun streamed in across the table. Marjory moved her pen in and out of the shadow.

'I have a delightful pleasure in view which is the thought of going to Braehead where I will walk to Craky-hall which puts me in mind that I walked to that delightful place with a delightful young man beloved by all his friends and especially by me as his loveress but I must not talk any longer about him for Isa said it is not proper for to speak of gentalman but I will never forget him I hope that at 12 or 13 years old I will be as learned as Miss Isa and Nancy Keith for many girls have not the advantage I have and I am very very glad that satan has not given bols and many other misfortunes.'

She paused. There was silence, for even the scratching of her pen had ceased. Outside a bird sang shrilly. Isa and Nancy sat with a pile of frothy white muslin between them, absorbed. The pins flashed in the sunlight as they stuck them in. Willie was reading with Help curled up at his feet. Looking at them like this, together and secure, a strange feeling came over the watching child. It had come to her before, just as suddenly, but never so strongly. In a flash she knew that she was threatened; life was not really peaceful and safe. It was treacherous and cruel. Her heart thumped, as it had done in the library at Kirkcaldy that hot summer's day when Isa first stepped into her life. She was frightened. It became suddenly necessary that she should tell them. The very sunlight quivered with urgency.

'Oh!' she said, in a horrified gasp.

They looked up startled. No-one else had noticed anything. She had turned a little pale, Isa thought, and made her move her chair out of the sun. Willie pulled down the blind, and the room became dim and shadowy. Nancy's bright hair and startled, greeny glittering eyes were the only points of brilliance now. The dog yelped suddenly as if he, too, had felt something pass through the room. He padded gently across to Isa, who patted him; smiled at Marjory, a deep, wise, *safe* smile. Hesitantly, then with relief, the child smiled back. Isa *knew*. Nothing really could happen to her while Isa was there, her 'gentle lover of nature'. 'Isa,' she said coaxingly, in a whisper, 'tell me Helvellyn.'

Softly, her hands folded because it was too shadowy to sew, Isabella began. Her light voice drifted like the rustling of leaves across the room. Nancy closed her eyes; even Willie laid down his book. Marjory tilted her chair forward eagerly, listening. Isa's quiet voice pulled her back into the real world again. When it stopped, her cheeks had grown pink again, and she was laughing at Help scratching her ear on the floor. The gong sounded for dinner, and she ran downstairs ahead of them chattering as gaily as usual. She seemed to have quite forgotten whatever it was that upset her. Just as suddenly as she had wanted to tell them her fear, she now wanted to hide it again. She had been flung off her guard for an instant, and her usual secrecy returned. She ate, sang, played all the rest of the day, as if nothing had happened, but her fear had not really gone. It lay somewhere in the darkest corner of her mind, and would come back. She would never be wholly free from it again.

That evening, she sat by the schoolroom window, painfully hemming round a white cambric handkerchief that was to be a present for Grandmamma, when she left Ravelston. It had been a good day after all, with no scenes to disturb the peace, and she was very pleased. She tried to pucker her forehead when she sewed, just like Isa. Willie was sitting with her, perched up on the settee in a way which was forbidden to Marjory. She was not allowed to jump on it, either, because this would injure the springs. Boys were always allowed to do more things than girls, and it was very unfair. Still, she liked Willie's company. It made her feel very grand to be sitting sewing like a grown-up lady, and making conversation with a young man. They were discussing the relative merits of bitches and dogs. Marjory had a definite opinion about this. At the moment her distress was great because a neighbour's dog had had five puppies and all were to be drowned but one. Marjory had not been to see them, she would not go. Her eyes filled with tears every time she thought of it.

'I would rather have a man dog than a woman dog,' she said decidedly, shaking her head, 'because they do not bear like woman dogs. It is a hard case; it is shocking.'

'No, but listen, Madgie,' said Willie, in an effort to console her. The door opened and Nancy looked in. She said, 'Bed, Madgie,' and went out again.

Marjory frowned and stamped her feet.

'Isa should come for me herself,' she said, tossing her head. 'I won't notice.'

Willie did not answer. He looked at her and began to whistle. The air burred with disapproval. Marjory did not care. She went over to the big work-box in the corner, with all the little work trays, and began to fold her work and put it slowly away. Her cheeks burned, but she would not look round even when the door opened again and Isa's voice said:

'Come, Madgie. It's bedtime. Did Nancy not call you?'

Marjory could not answer. Willie, swinging the tassel of the blind-cord to and fro, answered carelessly:

'She did, but you should summon Her Majesty yourself.'

At this, a swift, blind rage shook her from head to foot, as suddenly and violently as it had done in babyhood. She trembled, and clenched her hands.

'I won't go,' she said, in a tight, fierce, obstinate voice.

She slammed down the lid of the work-box and stamped her foot.

'Marjory,' said Isa quietly. 'Pray think what you are doing.'

Marjory looked at her, bitterly resentful. Isa looked calmly back. She seemed very serene and lovely, standing in a patch of pale evening sunshine, like a young and troubled Madonna. Marjory knew that she was anxious. She did not want her to fail. She did not want to do so herself, and yet she could not give in. There was silence, while she struggled, raged, then she turned away.

'I won't come. I won't,' she said.

'Oh, Willie . . .' Isa cried despairingly, but Willie got up off the sofa and said angrily, 'It's perfect nonsense, Madgie. Go with Isabella when she bids you go, or I'll put you out of the room myself!'

Marjory threw herself on the floor with a piercing shriek at this, and clung to it like a limpet, bellowing at the top of her voice. In spite of all she could do he picked her up as easily as one of the puppies, and carried her screaming and kicking, to the door. He put her down outside and gave her a hard push in the direction of the stairs.

'Now get away up to bed, and don't make another sound, you wild cat,' he told her, and slammed the door.

Marjory stood uncertainly for a minute, looking round her. She did not quite know whether to run back and hammer on the door until they let her in, or to go quietly upstairs after all. A sudden weariness came over her. She sat down on the step and began to cry, peacefully now, without temper. Isa found her there when she came upstairs, carrying the despised handkerchief, which had been flung to the ground in the struggle. She stopped. She had meant to be angry, as William told her she ought to be, and pass on without a word, but there was something tragic in Marjory's sorrow, which made it impossible. Instead, she held up her hand to help the child up, for she was crumpling her frock dreadfully, and found herself imprisoned in a tight hug.

'Oh, Isa,' whispered Marjory, overcome. 'I forgot. This was to have been my *good* Saturday. Oh, why does everything always go so wrong? What can I do?' she sounded in despair.

'You should ask God to help you, Marjory,' said Isa gravely. 'And forgive you. You have a most obstinate temper. You see how you hurt yourself with it, and those who love you, but you hurt God far more.'

'Yes, but I don't *know* God,' said Marjory, cheering up a little, and quite ready to argue the point. 'So it is not so bad. But I don't want to hurt you, Isabella, indeed I do not.'

'You can only get to know God by praying to him,' Isabella told her. She held out her hand. 'Come, I will hear you say your prayers to-night, and perhaps you will consider more carefully what you are saying, and to whom you are speaking.'

It was all very well, thought Marjory, but how could you speak to a person who never answered you? It was no good trying to argue with God, for he just wasn't there. She sighed. Of course, Isa must be right, because she was so good. As she went up the stairs, her hand most trustfully in Isa's, she felt suddenly sorry for God, who had no cousins at all to teach him, and yet was so good. All at once she decided to love him. It was funny how easy it was to love someone if you were sorry for them, although it was melancholy to consider that even with such a beautiful cousin as Isa, she could not even be a little good. She was suddenly filled with a great desire to pray and, loosing her hand, went skipping up the stairs ahead of Isa, calling out:

'Oh, *do* let's pray! Let's pray immediately.'

Isabella, coming more sedately behind her, felt a little bewildered. She could not suppose that this tremendous sense of devotion was altogether quite natural. However, she was anxious not to quench the child's ardour, for Marjory was inclined to forget her prayers if not constantly reminded, so she agreed. Marjory, kneeling in prayer, had an ardent, uplifted look that would have pierced the gates of heaven. She kept her hands folded, her head bent. Her lips formed the stiff words of the prayer with careful attention, but as to her thoughts, and why a sudden, secret smile flashed into her eyes and was gone, no-one could tell, not even her dear Isa.

Braehead

raehead was like nowhere else on earth. When she stood by the burn, a deep peace flew into her restless heart, and stilled it utterly. It almost ceased to beat, and the child to breathe, with the wonder of it. All around her, in the woods, the great leafy trees dropped their branches to the water, whispering secrets. The blue sky was flecked with small white clouds like puffs of smoke. It was a clear, fresh day, for it had rained in the night. Everything was brighter than reality. Marjory stood with her head flung up, like a pony; shadows of the leaves danced on her white dress, her hair, her bare arms, brown from a summer out of doors. She was sturdy and free like a pony, too. She would go her own way. Standing under the trees at beautiful Braehead, she suddenly folded her hands, and whispered up into the clear sky, as if she could reach beyond it:

'Make me good! You can! You can!'

It would be terrible if she behaved badly at Braehead. Isa would be extremely shocked, and so would Nancy. Willie would never forgive her if she did not behave in front of Isy Craufurd. She *had* to stop getting angry somehow. It was mostly peversity, tossing her head when asked to do something. stamping, and, when corrected or opposed, 'roaring like a bull', her old fault. It just seemed as if she could not help it, and she could not pray either. A great emptiness had overtaken her. She knelt obediently, under Isa's guidance, to a Being who could strike you dead in a moment, if he liked, and if you were wicked. Marjory listened. After a bit, she said:

'But God made us.'

'Well?' said Isa.

'If he made us, he could have made us good all the time as well—and if he didn't, I think he's silly!'

'Oh, Marjory,' said Isa reproachfully, sadly. Marjory was sorry. She was always sorry when she made Isa unhappy, and since talking about God seemed to do it, she did not talk about him any more. Nor did she pray. That is, she gabbled, and peeped between her fingers when she knelt beside Isa night and morning. She did not know that the intense, hidden thought drawn from her under the trees at Braehead, was prayer. At the moment, it was more like a demand. 'You've got to! You must,' urged Marjory, miserably, forcing God's hand. Nothing happened. She stood, defiant, under the big trees, and waited for the miracle that would make her good.

It did not come. Indeed, she grew worse. Not even Braehead, the beautiful and beloved, could keep her temper from rising, and confounding her. She dashed her cup of milk to the ground in front of the Miss Craufurds, because Isa would not let her have coffee instead, and they were shocked. That began it; afterwards nothing went right. It was Ravelston over again. Yet, always, there was Isa, the one good deed in a naughty world. Marjory loved her more and more. If it had not been for Isa, she could never have kept up the unequal struggle. Isa was very sad that she did not behave better, but she never gave up teaching, loving, restraining Marjory. Nancy went away on a visit, and did not come back for a long time. The Miss Craufurds, in a kind effort to please their difficult guest, invited Miss Bonner to play with her. Even this did not please her. Miss Bonner was stupid, and plain, and dull. She did not know any poetry and no interesting games. Marjory pushed her to and fro, and ordered her about, and she did not seem to mind. Only Isa noticed.

'You are not very kind to poor Miss Bonner, Madgie,' she said one day. 'It is not good in you, when you have so many pleasures and advantages that she has not.'

'Well, that is not my fault!' said Marjory, tossing her head.

109

★ *Part Three* ★

She was sitting on the schoolroom floor, playing with her pet canary. He was her very own, the most charming present she had ever had. She had taught him to hop on her finger and eat the seed from her hand, but no matter how prettily he played, Isa would not look. The silence was cold and unfriendly. Marjory heard her cousin close her book and get up from the chair. Now she was going to leave the room; it was very unfair. She scrambled to her feet and flew to the door to prevent it.

'You shan't go out! You shan't!' she cried, clinging to the door handle with all her might. Isa stopped and looked at her.

'I was not going out,' she said calmly. 'But I think that you, certainly, had better go to your room and stay there until you feel better.'

'I won't go,' said Marjory. She went and stood by the window. The canary hopped and pecked delicately in his cage, but she would not look at him any more. She stood with her hands clasped behind her back and her head in the air, looking the picture of obstinacy. Isa watched her for a moment in silence. At last she said:

'Marjory.'

The figure by the window seemed stiffer and crosser and even more obstinate, but did not move.

'Very well, Marjory,' said Isa at last. 'Then I shall go away.'

Marjory did not look round. She did not believe that Isa would really go.

The door shut.

In a moment, she turned. Her eyes flashed. She felt herself to be the most desolate, distressed child in all the world. Nobody understood her and everyone hated her. She flung herself on the ground, screaming, thumping the floor with her clenched fists. Her face grew scarlet, crumpled with rage. The canary fluttered wildly in his cage, but she did not care how she startled him. She did not care about anything. Her good resolutions had tumbled down like a pack of cards. She screamed, and howled, and rolled on the floor, because she wanted them all to hear her. She would disturb the whole house, until they

110

came to find out what was wrong. Yet, when at last the door
rattled and Isa came in she screamed out again and shouted:

'Don't dare to come in! Don't come near me!'

Nobody would want to come near such a disagreeable child,
the Miss Craufurds wondered how Isa could do it. She was
worried. She guessed, vaguely, at the turmoil and strife that
were tearing the child apart. It was growth. In Marjory it was
intenser, more violent, as everything was. She knew too, that
it must be something more, something that made her sigh when
Isa kissed her good night. She had come across her in the garden, with such a sad, unearthly look, not like a child at all.
Then it passed. In an instant she had become gay, laughing,
and talking nonsense; more of a child than still, prim little
Miss Bonner. And Marjory wanted to be good; she was stricken
each time with a fearful remorse that Isa dreaded as much as
the tantrum. May and Isy Craufurd, even kind old Mrs. Craufurd, advised her to punish the child severely, once and for all,
but she shook her head. She wanted to help her, not to add to
her distress. It was as if she saw Marjory with her life like a
tangled skein of wool, holding it out to her. What good would
scolding do? It could not untie the knots. It might even break
the trust and love that Isa knew was the one thing that might
save her. She was worried, too, at her own youth and inadequacy. Marjory thought her 'learned, witty, and sencable'.
She knew she was not. At that moment, listening outside the
schoolroom door to the screams and sobs within, she wanted
her mother most desperately.

She went in.

Marjory threw a book at her.

The moment it left her hand she knew what a dreadful thing
she had done. It fell on the floor at her feet, but Isa did not
move. Marjory, horror-struck, burst into tears, real tears of
sorrow and amazement at her own badness of heart. She
expected Isa to leave her for ever, but she only bent down,
picked up the book and put it back on the table. Then she said
gently:

'Marjory, go into your room and try to think over all your

111

actions this afternoon. Then wash your face with cold water, to take away the tears, and come back here. I will read to you, if you like.'

When the child, half unbelieving, had gone, she tidied the room and put back the cushions and books that Marjory, in her rage, had hurled on the floor. Then she took Helvellyn from its place on the shelf, and sat down by the open window. It was cool now in the evening. Autumn was slowly turning the green leaves to brown and red. The rowans were splendid with their bright scarlet berries. In the garden roses and dahlias were out together. She sat waiting, till the door opened, and the child came in. She had changed her dress to a clean white one, and tidied her hair. She looked solemn, tired out by the passion which had shaken her. She came and leaned against Isa, but Isa did not move.

'Forgive me, Isa,' she whispered, turning up her face for a kiss. 'I will never do it again, never, never.'

'But, Madgie,' said Isa gently; at her pet-name the child was less taut. 'How many times have you promised to think very carefully before. You said so last time.'

There was silence.

'Were you very much affronted, Isa?' she asked in a very small voice.

Isa nodded. 'I was never so much affronted in my life,' she declared. 'How could you do so, Madgie? And what will Nancy say to-morrow when she comes?'

Marjory looked at the floor.

'I never will do it again' she burst out. 'Never, never.'

She really meant it, but she always did. She meant it until that horrible rush of fury drowned all thought, and she opened her mouth and screamed with all her might. Sometimes her own screams startled her. She turned, and climbed on to Isa's lap. She was really getting too big now for such baby ways, but in moments of stress it was the only place she felt safe. Isa kept her there until she heard the bell, then she put her gently down on to the floor.

'It is time to go downstairs,' she said, but Marjory shook

112

her head. 'You go,' she urged, adding earnestly. 'I think I'll just stay here by myself for a while, and think.'

Isa smiled.

'Don't be too long, Muffy,' she said, and left her.

Alone, Marjory sat down by the canary cage, and sighed. She looked at the canary, and sighed again. Isa had told her once that being sorry was not enough. You should do something very hard as well, to make up for it, or give up something that you liked very much. Marjory looked more fierce and determined than ever, as the idea struck her. She would offer her dear canary to Miss Bonner, because she often was unkind to her, and she had not got so many toys. The idea made her feel better at once. Almost cheerful again, she ran down the stairs after Isa. Maggie, the maidservant, was standing at the foot of the stairs with a can of hot water. When she saw Marjory she exclaimed:

'Well, Miss Madgie, in trouble again, so I hear! I never saw a child like you. Here's Miss Craufurd saying she wonders how your cousin can stand you, playing your tricks the way you do. It's a wonder you're not sent home, I'm sure.'

'You don't know anything about it,' said Marjory, but she was shocked. She thought she could never go into the drawing-room when they all felt like that about her. It was terrible. She fetched her cloak from the hall, where it hung next to Isa's, and slipped out of the side door, and into the wood. The opinion of those around her mattered terribly to Marjory. She could never be happy if people did not love her. Standing in the wood at evening, with the sun just sinking behind the trees and shadows rustling in the leaves, she felt unutterably lost and sad. Sobs shook her and an utter desolation overcame her. She was alone, so alone that she did not hear footsteps coming up the path through the glen. She heard nothing until a voice said cheerfully:

'Well, Madgie, what are you doing here, like a sprite in the woods? Are you come to bewitch me?'

Turning, she saw Mr. Craigie smiling at her, and burst out:

'Please don't make fun of me. I'm so unhappy. I don't know what to do!'

At this, he grew serious at once. When Marjory cried, it was not as other children, like a summer shower, but deeply, inconsolably. It touched him. He drew her to a big tree-trunk fallen at the side of the path, and made her sit down beside him.

'Tell me when you like, and as much as you want to,' he told her. He offered her a very large handkerchief. She took it gratefully, and in another moment burst out:

'Ev-everybody just now hates me, and I deserve it, for I don't behave well.'

The thought of it overcame her completely, and the large handkerchief was wet and crumpled before she felt calm enough to tell him about the dreadful things she had done. He did not seem so appalled by them as she had expected.

'Isabella is by far too indulgent to me,' said Marjory pitifully. 'Even the Miss Craufurds say that they wonder at her patience with me and it is indeed true, for my temper is a bad one.'

'Well, but so is mine. I've got the devil of a temper,' said Mr. Craigie, looking very cheerful about it. 'But see here, Madgie, people don't hate one for it. They rather like it. The only thing is, one learns to control it a bit, like everything.'

'I don't!' said Marjory, in a wail. 'Isa tells me to pray, and that God will help me to flee from the devil, but I can't. I can't pray.'

She paused.

'I just say words,' she added sadly; wise enough to know that there was something more, if she could only find it.

Mr. Craigie looked round for a minute rather desperately, and then said:

'I don't know much about praying and all that sort of thing, Madgie, your cousin Isa is the best person for that. But I'll tell you one thing. You don't have just to speak to God when you kneel by your bed at night, you know. He's everywhere, ready to listen. When you see a lovely day, or you're very happy

114

about something, so that you feel grateful as well as glad—you know what I mean?'

She nodded, intent, holding back her tears.

'Well, that's a sort of prayer too. In fact, it's the very best sort. It's what you *feel* that really matters, not the words so much. Understand?'

'Oh, yes!' she said gratefully. 'I often feel that way—glad, and—and just as if I wanted to thank somebody. I never thought of it as a prayer.' She looked at him with her big solemn eyes. 'You must be a very good person, Mr. Craigie,' she said at last.

No-one would have thought of Georgie Craigie like that. He was so careless and gay, and made everything into a joke, as if nothing mattered. Perhaps he felt it himself, for he grew very red and burst out, 'Good Lord, no!' as if the very idea confounded him. Marjory was surprised. To be good was the greatest thing, the unattainable. Very few people were really good; her own list was headed by Mary Queen of Scots and Isa. As they got up from the tree-trunk, and walked in silence down through the woods towards the house, she added Mr. Craigie. She was glad he was good. When they reached the gate into the garden, she paused.

'Mr. Craigie,' she said, standing on tip-toe to see his face better, for he was very tall. 'Do you think that if there was ever a person who found they loved another friend or a relation best in the world, even more than their parents, they would be wicked people? Would they?

Mr. Craigie looked down at her. Looked for a long time. At last he said: 'No, Marjory. It would not be wicked. One loves, naturally, the people who do the most for us, and whom we like to be with the best. It may be our parents, or it may not. When you grow up, it will be the man you marry. To honour your parents is a different thing. It just means loving them as much as you can, being kind and thoughtful to them.'

There was a pause.

'I see,' said Marjory, while he still watched her. What a strange, serious little creature she was! Yet, when she ran and played in the fields, she was a child, with nothing sad or precocious about her. He had thought her easier to understand than most little girls, because when she asked questions she waited for the answer, and listened to it. Yet who could tell what thoughts were hidden away inside her, behind that fierce, grave face? For a moment he felt nonplussed. Certainly he did not know what his explanation had done for her. Only, as he watched, the solemn look gave way to relief. She smiled up at him gladly.

'Come!' she said. 'We'll be late!'

In a flash, she was away from him down the garden. He saw her white dress fluttering between the flower beds as he followed, wondering. She had quite forgotten him now. She felt gay, and good again. As she ran, laughing, up to the door, she called 'Isa, Isa.'

PART IV

PART IV

Edinburgh and Braehead
Spring—Autumn 1810

Marjory spent nearly the whole winter at Braehead, and she was happy, though her journal finished on a sad note of repentance. She was glad it was finished. She pressed it tightly shut with both hands, and told Isa that she never wanted to see it again. It contained nothing but quarrels and scenes from beginning to end, and shamed her when she read it. 'I never will write another!' she declared with a sigh, and wise Isa said nothing. Only, on their return to Edinburgh just after Marjory's seventh birthday she laid a new exercise book out on the schoolroom table, neatly ruled.

She had changed; not only because she had lost a front tooth, which made Isabella sigh, but she seemed to be stronger, more determined. She looked deeper into things. Isa saw this, as she saw everything. To other people, the child had simply grown, and improved. She left her tempers behind when she returned, and nothing was said about them; even Nancy kept quiet. They seemed to have passed away like the winter storms. Spring came, with cold winds and bright sunshine. Marjory grew gay, happy, and carefree again. She became more forbearing to the children in the Square, and kinder to everyone. The struggle was passed; the growth accomplished. Isa, relieved, ruled up the journal, and set beside it a new quill pen.

Marjory learned fast, as she always did when she was happy. She read, as usual, a great variety. The *Arabian Nights* pleased her, and filled her mind with beautiful impressions, and rich, new words. She enjoyed words. She liked parts of Thomson's

119

Seasons, and a rather melancholy poem of his about Celadon
and Amelia, and then turned with equal pleasure to Mrs.
Trimmer's *Fabulous Histories*, a book of moral stories about
birds. The deepest, most absorbing thing at the moment was
history, in which she was studying with remarkable intensity
the life of Mary Queen of Scots. This queen had always filled
Marjory with admiration. She thought her 'beautiful and
angelick' and her adventures very romantic indeed. She dis-
cussed it with Isabella by the hour, and they read books together, until the Queen of Scots became almost as real as the
people round about, and far more fascinating. At the end of the
lesson, when Isa had laid down the book, she took it up and
gazed with a curious mixture of awe and delight at the frontis-
piece, which was rather a stiff, old-fashioned picture of Mary
praying on the night before her execution.

'Poor, poor, Mary!' said Marjory sadly.

Nancy laughed. She very often did laugh at anything melancholy or dramatic. Marjory sometimes thought her cousin
Nancy lacked feeling. It was the moment to practise self-
control. She put the book carefully back on the table, and
marched out of the room without saying a word, but bursting
with indignation all the time. In a moment, it was forgotten.
To-day was wash-day, and she coaxed Nana to let her have
some soap-suds in a blue enamel basin, in which to wash her
dolls' clothes. Her dolls were neglected most of the time, but on
washing-day they had a wonderful time. It was a bright spring
day with warm sunshine, and Marjory carried them out to the
back green, and set to work. Nana tied a large apron round her
waist, to prevent splashing, and she was perfectly happy. The
dolls lay tumbled on the grass. Marjory kindly wrapped them
in a shawl and set them up at their own table. She had two
dolls' tables, and a stool, made from dark shiny mahogany. She
splashed the suds everywhere, and rubbed and scrubbed with
an anxious expression as she had seen Nana do.

Presently Nancy came out. She stood beside the tub, watching. Perhaps she looked a little envious, but all she said was:

'Isa wants you. She's got a letter.'

John Balfour Esq.r offered
to kifs me, & offered to marry
me though the man wases-
pused, & his wife was prsent, &
said he must ask her per
-mision but he did not I
think he was ashamed or con
founded before 3 gentelman
M.r Jobson & two M.r Kings
Isabella teaches me to read my
bible & tells me to be good and
say my prayers, and every
thing that is nesary for a
good carecter and a good con
-science. ——

Facsimile of a page from the Journal
In the possession of the National Library of Scotland

Marjory did not answer. She did not intend ever to speak to Nancy again. Not that her cousin seemed to care, she scooped up a handful of the light, bright suds and, carelessly, began to blow bubbles through her fingers. She blew the most beautiful bubbles. They floated away across the narrow strip of garden, out of sight. Sometimes they burst. Marjory stood watching, filled with rapture. Presently she burst out:

'Please, please, Nan! Let me make some! Show me how.'

'Like this—watch!' ordered Nancy, scooping up more suds. Marjory obediently did the same. She followed all Nancy's movements exactly, but the bubbles would not come. She got suds on her nose and into her mouth, but she had not made a single bubble. Nancy made dozens. The air was full of them when Isa came out, carrying a letter.

'Your father is coming to see you. He has business in Edinburgh,' she began, and then laughed. 'Oh, Madgie, what have you been doing? You've even got suds in your hair.'

'Nan's blowing bubbles,' explained Marjory, as proudly as if she had made them herself.

'Let me!' said Isa eagerly. She knelt down beside Nancy and gathered up a handful of suds. Soon, the bubbles floated away from between her fingers, up into the blue sky. They all watched, laughing. Marjory looked at her cousins, kneeling together beside the tub, in the sun and shadow of the first spring day.

'I'll never forget how it was,' she thought suddenly, for no reason. 'Never, never. I'll remember it all my life.'

And so she did.

Her father spent four days in Edinburgh. Marjory was delighted; she had so much to show and tell. He was not fussy and critical as her mother would have been, and he listened to all the things she told him when they went out for walks together. Her mother never really listened when you told her anything; you thought she did, and then all at once she asked you a question about something quite different, and usually dull. Her father was not like that. At first, after so long, she was a little stiff with him, but they soon dropped back into their old, affectionate companionship. She could speak to him about nearly everything, and she did. She told him about Brae-head, revealing at once her deep love for it, and for all the people in her new life. She let him read her journal, and see all her lesson books. He found her much improved in everything, grown in mind and spirit as well as in body. She had left him a baby, spoilt and self-willed. He met her again as a child, with a personality and ideas of her own. She knew her own faults, and she fought her own battles with them. He was proud of her. He was proud of Isabella, too, who had made this happen. Love drew everything from Marjory; she responded instantly to it. Her father saw at once how deeply she had become part of this life. He did not resent it. He had known that either she would languish, and ask to come home, or she would thrust down roots, deeply, into the new soil.

'Well, Maidie,' he said. 'So you're happy with your cousins. You don't want me to take you home when I go?'

Her face clouded. She came and leaned against him.

'I love you very much, Father,' she whispered softly.

She did not say she would like to come home.

The next day he left. He came back to Kirkcaldy laden with gifts and messages from Marjory. If the child had wanted to come, he would have brought her, but she did not. Maidie was a wise child, a child to be trusted. She should do as she chose.

Mrs. Fleming thought differently. Her letters to Isa Keith became slightly acid, reading between the lines. On the surface they were bright, as they had always been. Isa knew what had happened; she had expected it. The first casual, bitter seed had been sown. It was only a question of time before the golden cage must open, and the bird fly home.

Marjory was perfectly happy. She celebrated her father's visit by a sudden burst of poetry, which she wrote in her journal the day after he left. She called it:

'An address to my Father when he came to Edinburgh.

'My father from Kirkcaldy came but not to plunder or to game. Gaming he shuns I am very sure. He has a heart that is very pure.

> Honest and well behaved is he
> And busy as a little Bee.'

She had not known it was a poem till she was half-way through; it had just flown into her head like that. She was pleased. From that time on, she wrote poetry on every occasion. It was a *new* accomplishment, and she liked to use it. Bending over the table till her nose nearly touched the paper, she clutched the pen firmly and guided it between the lines. You had to write poetry clearly, and in lines one under the other, as it was printed in books.

Isa, watching, sighed.

Now it was summer, 1810. Marjory watched Nana take out her light dresses from the top of the big wardrobe in Isa's room. They were wrapped in layers of tissue paper, and scented deliciously with lavender. With them came a round white box containing her two straw bonnets, an everyday one and a Sunday one. When she wore them last, she was at Braehead. A year ago! How much could happen in that time. Why, a year ago she had been only six years old, and not good at all. Nana shook out a sprigged blue muslin and held it up against her with a sigh. Marjory stood still. She remembered playing in the hayfields with Isa and Mr. Craigie in this dress.

'They must be lengthened, every one of them!' said Nana, with a sigh, and added, 'How you do grow, to be sure, Miss Madgie.'

Grow! Well, of course she did, in a whole year. Nana was silly to be so much surprised. Marjory stood still, thinking. Presently she said:

'Do you think—*soon*—we'll go to Braehead again?'

Nana shut the doors of the wardrobe, and gathered up the dresses.

'Wait and see, child,' she said. It was all she ever said.

Marjory waited and waited. She knew just what the invitation would be like when it came, written in Miss Craufurd's pretty, spiky handwriting. She watched the courier anxiously, but nothing happened. At last, running into the dining-room at dinner, when everyone else was already seated, she saw that the letter had come, and her aunt was reading it. She slid into her place, and folded her hands for grace. There was a minute's silence. Isa cut some toast into fingers for her.

'Amen!' shouted Marjory triumphantly, and added quickly, 'Aunt, are we going to Braehead soon?'

Mrs. Keith laid down the letter, and smiled.

'Yes, Madgie,' she said. 'You are. Eat your dinner, and I'll tell you about it.'

'Mamma!' protested Nancy, shaking her head. 'You never used to tell *us* when we asked!' She looked at Marjory and whispered, her eyes dancing like points of fire, 'Spoilt brat!'

Marjory glared.

Mrs. Keith read out the letter. Margaret Craufurd wrote that she was sorry, but at first it might only be possible to have Marjory for two days, as there was not a room for her. Willie and Isabella, who were now married, would also be of the party and she was much looking forward to having the whole family together. It would be like old times.

'Oh, *Isa*,' said Marjory in a wail. She had turned quite pale, and the whole room swam in a mist of tears. Only two days at her beautiful Braehead and then to come back, alone, to the heat and dust of the town at midsummer. It was too terrible.

'I'm not surprised,' Nancy declared, shaking her curls. 'The way you behaved last year! It's a wonder they asked you at all.'

Marjory did not hear. Her heart was broken. It was too much to bear. Her piteous, crumpled face touched even Nancy into silence. She looked down at her plate while big tears splashed, unheeded, on to her pudding. This was tragedy. When Marjory cried, you never expected to see her smile again. Isa leaned towards her.

'Don't cry, Madgie,' she whispered. 'If you are brave, and let everyone see how much more sensible you have become, I dare say something can be arranged. Perhaps, if there is no room, you can sleep with me. We'll see about it when we arrive.'

Marjory did not answer. Sobs shook her. She only turned, and put her arms round Isa's neck.

It was quite a week before they left, with all the packing and preparations that were to be done. Marjory became quite used to the thought that she might not be able to stay long. Though she lamented the fact several times in her journal, she was not too sorry, for she was sure that Isa would manage. She complained more for the look of the thing, than because she believed her doom was sealed. In the last few days lessons became quite erratic; sometimes there were none at all. Marjory got out her journal, unasked, and wrote a poem.

> *Beautious Isabella say*
> *How long at Braehead will you stay*
> *O for a week or not so long*
> *Then weel desart the busy throng*
> *Ah can you see me sorrow so*
> *And drop a hint that you must go*
> *I thought you had a better hart*
> *Than make me with my dear friends part*
> *But now I see that you have not*
> *And that you mock my deradful lot*
> *My health is always bad and sore*
> *And you have hurt it a deal more.*

'The reason I write this poem is because I am going to Braehead only two days.'

They drove to Braehead on a real summer's day with a bright blue sky, and the big trees hanging limp and golden against it. It was not the best day for a journey. When the windows were shut it was too hot, and when they were opened clouds of white dust flew in from the road. The heat, and the lurching movement of the carriage, made everyone cross. Luckily it did not take more than two hours. Marjory was breathless with excitement when they drove through the gates and up the avenue. She jumped from side to side. There was the hayfield, and the woods, and the house. The creeper was green now, but in autumn it turned bright scarlet; she hoped they would stay long enough to see it this year. There were roses in the front flower-beds. She blew a delighted kiss to the four yew-trees, two of which Isa had laughingly named 'Lot and his wife'. She was coming home. It did not matter what anyone said, what righteous facts they might produce, Braehead was home to Marjory. It was the delight of her soul.

The carriage stopped. She jumped out, and was up the steps in a flash. How cool and dim it was in the house, after the bright sunlight. The air was fragrant with bowls of crimson roses, and pot pourri. It felt clean and beautiful after the town. Dancing upstairs after Isa, she had quite forgotten that there was to be a time limit to her happiness. She need not have worried. Margaret was delighted to have Marjory, if Isa would not mind sharing the bed; it was just that, for the moment, all the other rooms were occupied. Isa, looking at Marjory's anxious face, said she did not mind at all.

Soon, the days slipped into place. Marjory did lessons, but there was no schoolroom for her this time. She sat on the grass, and read about Mary Queen of Scots with Isa. It was impossible to do anything serious. Mr. Craigie came over nearly every day, to join her cousins, and the Craufurds. They all sat in the garden while the lessons were in progress. Marjory thought it a great joke. They did her sums for her and recited poetry, which kept her amused. Sometimes they all walked to the seaside, taking lunch and tea. Marjory ran up and down the beach, and splashed in and out of the water. Isa tucked her dress up into her sash, but it always got wet. She grew strong and plump, and had an enormous appetite. On very clear days, Mr. Craigie told her, you could see right across the bay to Kirkcaldy.

'But I don't want to!' said Marjory, frowning. It was the first shadow that had come over the day. To chase it away, she threw back her head and laughed aloud. She buried her feet and legs in the hot, golden sand. She kept very still. Then, suddenly, up she sprang, scattering it all.

'Let's make a very big castle,' she suggested, at just about the hottest part of the day. Nobody sounded enthusiastic. She began it herself. It had grown quite big by the time, one by one, they came to help her. The day grew cooler, less fiery. The heap of sand grew larger. It became a proper castle with battlements and a drawbridge, like the one that had imprisoned Mary, Queen of Scots.

'It's beautiful!' said Marjory, when it was done. At the end, she had tired of it quicker than they did, and gone off by herself to look for pebbles and shells. Mr. Craigie caught her up, and swung her in the air. He was very strong. He sat her down right on the top of the sand-castle.

'You can be Queen of the Castle!' he said. 'Mary, Queen of Scots, if you like it!'

Marjory wriggled free, and jumped off again, shaking her head.

'I don't want to die young!' she said. Looking round at the whispering sea and the bright sand, she said suddenly:

'I want to live for ever and ever!'

Waking every morning filled with this intense happiness and goodness; it was impossible to lie still beside the sleeping Isa. Wide-awake Marjory wondered at Isa's capacity for sleep. She herself was always awake. She lay waiting for Isa to come to bed every night and woke before her every morning. Her mind was as restless as her body. She was like a flame. Words and songs flowed through her head like a stream. Sometimes she remembered them, and wrote them down later in the day. Though lessons had really been dropped for the summer, she wrote in her journal still. It was full of poetry now, because she was happy. She had to sing.

> *To days ago was the King's birthday*
> *And to his health we sung a lay*
> *Poor man his health is very bad*
> *And he is often very mad*
> *He was a very comely lad*
> *Since death took his girl from his sight*
> *He to her grave doth walk at night*

★ *Part Four* ★

His son the grand grand Duke of York
I am sure he eaeth plenty pork
For I do hear that he is fat
But I am not so sure of that.

Marjory was not shy. She put down her thoughts boldly for everyone to see. At seven she knew perfectly well how to make her audience laugh with her. Under their laughter she knew, too, that they thought her clever. Indeed, she overheard Miss Craufurd telling Isa so, but had too much sense to let the knowledge run away with her, though she enjoyed it. In the joy of being able to write poetry, she composed verses on every occasion, to be read by the whole house. When three of the turkeys died, she wrote an ode and dedicated it tactfully to her hostess. This was amusing for everybody, but when she played in the woods, beside the little stream, or went walking down to the old bridge hand in hand with Isa, another Marjory woke inside her. She tried, afterwards, to put her feelings into words, her love of Braehead and the trees there; of Isa, whose presence made everything lovelier. It was too difficult. She struggled for expression, but only the littlest part of it could be written.

The lofty trees their heads do shake
When the wind blows a noise they make
When they are cut a crash you hear
That fills your very soul with fear,
Tis like the thunders loudest roar
You would not like to hear much more
It makes the earth begin to quake
And all its mity pillars shake
The viabration of the sound
Will I am sure you quite confound
It makes the mountains to resound.

When she stood under the great trees at Braehead she was filled with a tremendous love for the clean, sweeping wind that tossed the branches up and down. After summer, when the days

128

grew shorter the leaves turned brown, and fell, and were even more beautiful. She wanted to keep them for ever and ever like this. The shadow of parting fell on her. However much she pretended and longed for it, this was not her home. North Charlotte Street was not her home. One day, suddenly, the strange beings that ruled her life, would take her away as inexplicably as they had sent her. She saw that. It explained the sudden panic that swept over her so unexpectedly as it had done at Ravelston. It came more often now, and left her sick with dread. This, she did not tell. She never wrote about it. When it had passed, leaving her free and light-hearted again, she turned back to her everyday life with relief. She walked with Isa and Nancy, catching the leaves as they fell; she began her lessons again in a corner of the sitting-room, beside the fire. There, curled up beside the leaping flames with Help at her feet, she wrote her journal; wrote, with instinct, of the familiar things she did, in the sheltering peace of Braehead.

> *When cold as clay and cold as ice*
> *To get into a bed tis nice*
> *It is a nice thing for to creep*
> *But not to doze away and sleep*
> *Into a bed where Isa lies*
> *And to my questions she replies*
> *Corrects my faults improves my mind*
> *And tells me of the faults she find*
> *But she is sound asleep sometimes*
> *For that I have not got good rimes*
> *But when awake I teize her much*
> *And she doth squall at every touch*
> *Then Isa reads in bed alone*
> *And reads the fasts by good Nelson*
> *Then I get up to say my prayers*
> *To get my porridge and go downstairs.*

It was the happiest time of her life.

PART V

PART V

Kirkcaldy
July—December 1811

The room was very still. Crimson curtains shut out the gusty July evening. There was only one candle, in a twisted silver stand. It cast a bright light, that mingled with the dull glow of the fire, for though summer, it was cold and wet towards nightfall. Marianne Keith opened her work-box. It was her favourite time of the day, this hour before bedtime which she kept to herself. She read poetry, or wrote letters, or sometimes lay staring at the fire, looking back into her life. To-night, for no reason, she felt restless. There was no peace in the room. The candle burned, the heavy curtains shut her off securely from the world; there is nothing so safe as velvet curtains; but it was not enough. Her fingers moved nervously, untangling a skein of silk. Everything seemed to have stopped, holding its breath. Even the clock had ceased to tick, as if it were waiting too. She was glad when she heard footsteps in the passage outside; there was silence, then a light tap on the door. She lifted her head.

'Come in, Isabella,' she said.

The girl came in, surprised. She closed the door carefully behind her. Standing against the white panels, her dark hair gleamed; her eyes were dark too; only her dress of royal blue silk splashed against the quiet shadows, like a pebble flung in a pond.

'Did you guess, Mamma?' she said, and laughed. Again the shadows were startled; the silence pressed back after the sound had died away, more intently than before. Marianne put the

133

skein away and motioned her daughter to sit down. Shutting the lid of the work-box with a snap she said cautiously:

'I know this is hard on you, Isa, but you knew it would have to come. We put the day off as long as we could, but I can do no more. In any case, whenever it happened, it would be hard, I know.'

Isa shrugged her shoulders impatiently. At the first sign of sympathy she drew away. She came and knelt down by the fire, stirring it into flame.

'I don't care for myself,' she said resolutely, her face turned away. 'I care only for Marjory. I know it is best. After all, Aunt is her mother; she had a right to ask for her.'

She paused and her voice shook. 'But, Mamma, it has meant so much to her. Every night this week she has cried, and, when I've come upstairs she's been lying awake. She doesn't *want* to go. This is her home. It's cruel to send her away.'

The flame, set free, leaped up suddenly. Isa, leaning towards it, glowed; her eyes shone.

'You let me bring her here,' she said bitterly. 'And to-morrow you'll let her go home again, just like that. You know she'll be miserable. She suffers now. And how about Aunt? She didn't understand her before, you said so yourself. I suppose you think she has learned to know her better, after three years of separation.'

The flame dropped down, as suddenly as it had come. Isa's face was in shadow, her hands still, fallen into her lap. There was silence, while Marianne watched her. The air stirred with her rage and her helplessness.

'Whatever we feel, Isa, Marjory is her mother's child,' she said. 'We cannot refuse to let her go. I tried to tell you this when she came, but it made no difference then. You will see, when you have your own children.'

Isa bent her head, she said softly:

'Marjory is like that. If she goes away, I'll never see her again.'

'Nonsense, Isa. Don't be dramatic.' Marianne spoke sharply. 'My sister will let her come to us for the holidays, and I think she's right. As it is, she has become a stranger to her child; no mother will stand for that—nor for having her place taken by a chit of a girl. As Marjory's mother, what else do you expect? And as your own mother, I confess I think you need a holiday, Isa. You've been a perfect slave to that child for three years. I admire you for it. I think no other girl of your age would have done as much, but now it is time you had a change, as well as Marjory.'

Isabella sighed. She kept her head turned away, but she felt her mother's eyes watching her, calm, wise, understanding. You could argue with Isa: she listened. She did not toss away in a temper, like Nancy, or hold her hands over her ears. As a child, convinced, she would fling herself on to the floor, sobbing, 'You're right! You're right!' Now she stood very still, her hands clenched, her hair glinting like Nancy's in the firelight. She was twenty years old, 'learned, witty, and sensible'. Inside her still a little girl was screaming passionately: 'You're right! You're right.'

'Come, Isa,' said Marianne gently. She pulled her unresisting to the settee. Isa would not answer. She allowed herself to be touched but no more. She would not smile. At last, twisting the skein of silk in her fingers, she said hurriedly:

'I know that is true, Mamma. Often I've felt it a burden to have Madgie always to teach, or look after, when I wanted to amuse myself. She is not an easy child. But I said I would do it. I know—Mamma, I *know*, she is not an ordinary child. She's so wild, so sensitive. There are times that I've felt in her—something. I cannot explain.'

She was silent, thinking of that wet autumn night three years ago, when Marjory came. The room, only, had stayed the same, untouched. Whatever happened, it took no part. The clock ticked. Candle and fire burned. A child came, grew, and went away.

Marianne sighed.

'Where is she?'

Isa looked defiant.

'She's—in my room. She was crying—the long journey to-

135

morrow, you know! I thought it best.' She paused, and added with dignity, 'I would not in the ordinary way give in to her, of course.'

'Of course not,' said Marianne.

Isa looked relieved. She flew up from the settee, kissed her mother. In an instant she was gay, even casual again.

'Good night, Mamma.'

'Good night, Isa.'

It was dark on the stairs. The bedroom was lit by the pale glow of a night-light, set in a saucer. Marjory lay on the bed, wrapped in a shawl. She had fallen sideways, asleep. Her lashes lay dark against her cheek, and were still wet. Next door, the big trunk lay packed and corded. Isa undressed by the night-light. She moved silently, so as not to disturb the child. When all was done, she drew out the thin exercise books from the drawer where they were kept and read them over for the last time, close to the flame. All through the winter Marjory had been writing poetry. She had begun, after much thought, a long poem on Mary Queen of Scots. It nearly filled the book, and had taken a great deal of time and trouble, and rhyming, before it was done. The facts were correct, and a great deal of personal opinions wedged in as well. What would they think of it in Kirkcaldy? Turning the pages she came upon one of Marjory's odes, this time on the monkey, written, half in joke, to celebrate his birthday.

> *O lovely O most charming Pug*
> *Thy graceful air and heavenly mug*
> *The beauties of his mind do shine*
> *And every bit is shaped so fine*
> *Your very tail is most devine*
> *Your teeth is whiter than the snow*
> *You are a great buck and a bow*
> *Your eyes are of so fine a shape*
> *More like a christians than an ape*
> *His cheeks is like the roses blume*
> *Your hair is like the ravens plume*

> *His noses cast is of the roman*
> *He is a very pretty woman*
> *I could not get a rhyme for roman.*
> *So was obliged to call it weoman.*

This was quite a new joke, and Marjory thought it a very good one. She used it again in her next long poem, the last she had written, rather grandly called 'The Life of the King Jamess'.

> *At Perth poor James the first did die*
> *That wasn't a joy and luxury*
> *And the poor King was murdered there*
> *The nobles to do this did dare*
> *For he to check their power had tried*
> *This effort made did hurt their pride*
> *The second James was not so good*
> *To break his promise I know he would*
> *He once did say unto an earl*
> *He would not bring him into perl*
> *He bid him come to Stirling Castle*
> *In this James behaved like a rascle*
> *Upon the Kings word he relied*
> *And to the castle he then hied*
> *He wished him to give up the confedracy*
> *I would have dont if I were he*
> *The earl refused to do that thing*
> *At this quite furious was the King*
> *He put his sword into his guts*
> *And gave him many direfull cuts*
> *He vassals all to arms ran*
> *Their leader was a cowardly man*
> *From the field he ran in terror*
> *I must say this was an great error*
> *He was killed by a cannon splinter*
> *In the middle of the winter*
> *Perhaps it was not at that time*
> *But I could get no other rhyme*

James the third was very mean
And with mean persons was seen
He loved others more than his nobels
That was the cause of all his troubles
Very much he them insulted
And he seldom them consulted
For a long time this he had done
At last they got his youthfull son
And in battle he did engage
Though he was fifteen years of age
They marched against the very King
For having been both bad and mean
James the thirds life ends this way
Of his faults take care I say
James the fourth was a charming prince
We have not got a better since
In flodden field alas fell he
The Lords were vexed this to see
Thus fell a good King and a brave
He fell untimely to his grave
James the fifth loved favourites too
Which was a thing he should not do
At Pinkey were his armies killed
And with triumph they were not filled
He died of grief and of despair
His nobles for this did not care
Thus fell five kings most crually
When I hear of them I'm ready to sigh
A King I should not like to be
I'd be frightened for a conspiracy.

Isa closed the book. The night-light, flickering in a pool of wax, flared up brighter than day. For one brief moment she saw the sleeping child beside her stir in the sudden radiance, and turn away. Then, in an instant, the flame sank, wavered, and went out.

Next day Marjory returned home. Isa and Nancy accom-

panied her to the shore, and told her not to forget them. She
nodded as solemnly as if it were possible. It was another grey,
rainy day, and Nancy was cross. She snapped just as she
always did, but Marjory knew that this was her way of parting, and was grateful. If Nancy had softened she might have
flung herself at Isa and sobbed to be taken back. It was no
good. The boat was there, and she was in it.

'Be good, Muffy,' said Isa, and kissed her. The last thing she
saw was Isa's handkerchief, fluttering out across the stretch of
tossing grey water between them. Now it was only a white
speck on the shore, and now it was nothing. She turned away,
so white and desperate that several kind-hearted ladies were
moved to pity.

'Ye'll be off to school, no doubt?' they asked her.

'No,' said Marjory. 'I'm going home.'

Her father met her at Kinghorn, and then it was better. He
knew exactly how she would feel, and his conversation was just
right. He bought her a bun to eat, with sugar on top, in case
she was hungry. She slipped her hand in his, and they sat like
that most of the way. It was, after all, rather fun to come back
home a travelled young lady. Everyone looked at her. There
was so much to see and to hear that she was quite bewildered.
The first few days were gone in a flash. Her sister Isabella had
grown; she was now eleven, and Marjory did not share a room
with her any more. The baby was fat and charming; she liked
it better than anyone else. She took it into her arms and
whispered to it that she was feeling lost, and a little strange, as
if she, too, had wandered back into her babyhood. Everyone
was very kind to her. For the first few days she did as she
pleased; Isy listened willingly to stories of town life, and the
beauties of Braehead. They went for a picnic to Raith, and
Marjory was delighted.

At last, however, the strangeness wore away. Life became
normal, and Marjory was expected to become part of it. She
did her lessons with Isabella, sitting one each side of the round
table, as they had always done. Marjory was far ahead of her
sister. She thought it a great shame to be kept back for her. To

tell the truth, ever since her return from Edinburgh, she had got into the habit of finding fault with everything new. She would not eat this, because she never did at her aunt's. It was 'At Edinburgh I did this', and 'Isabella always does that' a hundred times a day. Now, swinging her legs against the table while her sister was trying to write,

'That is a silly history book. No wonder Isy can't learn. Isa says . . .'

Mrs. Fleming looked at her. Marjory looked impudently back. Her eyes danced. She kicked the table harder and harder.

'Marjory!' said her mother suddenly. Her voice made the child jump; she stopped swinging her legs and stared. 'I forbid you to mention your cousin to me again. You are not at Edinburgh now. I'm sick and tired of the very word Isabella.'

Marjory bent her head. Her cheeks burned, and yet a chill went through her. Didn't Mother like Isa? Why had she looked like that? Even placid Isy stopped writing, startled. She looked up, her mouth open. Mrs. Fleming left the room; perhaps she had said more than she intended. Marjory lifted her head. She stared out of the window, and suddenly, desperately, was afraid. It was July, and Isa and Nan would be going to Braehead. She could see the beautiful trees in the glen, the tumultuous, churning mill-wheel, the seashore at Barnbougle. Two large tears rolled down her cheeks.

Isabella stared at her, a little shyly. She was sorry Marjory was unhappy, but she could think of nothing that would comfort her. She bent her head over her exercise and wrote assiduously, pushing away the sight of her small sister's grief. Marjory struggled with her tears. She clenched her hands. One sob escaped, and Isy looked up in spite of herself.

'Don't, Maidie,' she said awkwardly. 'Mother didn't mean it, you know.'

'Oh, Isy,' said Marjory in a wail. 'I do—I do love cousin Isa!'

'Do you?' said Isabella, wondering. She had never loved anyone enough to cry for them. She looked at Marjory and then

140

went on with her exercise. After a few minutes Marjory also took up her pen, and a sheet of paper. Her sobs died away. She was very quiet. Her thoughts, her homesickness, tumbled on to the paper almost quicker than she could write.

> *I am now in my native land*
> *And see my dear friends all at hand*
> *There is a thing that I do want*
> *With you these beauteous walks to haunt*
> *We would be happy if you would*
> *Try to come over if you could*
> *Then I would quite happy be*
> *Now and for all eternity*
> *Isa is so very kind*
> *A better girl I could not find*
> *My mother is so very sweet*
> *And checks my appetite to eat*
> *My father shews us what to do*
> *But I am sure that I want you*
> *I should be happy you to see*
> *For I am sure that I love thee*
> *You are the darling of my heart*
> *With you I cannot bear to part*
> *The watter falls we go to see*
> *I am as happy as can be*
> *In pastures sweet we go and stray*
> *I could walk there quite well all day*
> *At night my head on turf could lay*
> *There quite well could I sleep all night*
> *The moon would give its tranciant light*
> *I have no more of poetry*
> *O Isa, do remember me,*
> *And try to love your Marjory.*
>
> Kirkcaldy, 26*th July* 1811.

It was a cry of despair. When she had finished it, she laid down her pen, quietened. Outside, the sun shone. She saw her father cross the garden on his way in to dinner, and sprang up, shaking the table again. 'Father! Father!' He waited for her. She came running out of the house, still with her pinafore on. He did not seem to mind but took her hand, gravely, as if she had been very much older. If he saw the traces of tears on her cheek, he said nothing. He led her away from the house. Together, they walked in the garden. He picked a rose, a red one, and gave it to her. She was not allowed to pick the roses herself. She took it, and smiled up at him.

'Oh thank you. It's beautiful,' she said, burying her nose, freckles and all, inside it. 'Isa says . . .'

She stopped. He raised his eyebrows.

'Father . . .' she said in a rush.

'Well, Maidie?'

'Do you mind if I speak about Isa? She just—she just comes into my mind.'

He looked at her. It was a kind, wise look. She smiled.

'Just speak of what makes you happy, Maidie,' he said, and gave her another rose. Now she had two. She looked at them for a long time, considering. She had almost forgotten what it was she wanted to know, although it was very important.

'I think I shall give one to Mother,' she said, at last.

In September, the dancing class opened again after the summer. It was decided that Marjory should go to it. Isabella had been attending for over a year, and was considered one of the best pupils there. Marjory was not very fond of dancing, and, as she grew, she was inclined to be clumsy. Gone were the days when she would dance before an audience.

'I don't want to go,' she said and, before she could hold it back, 'Isa never made me.'

Mrs. Fleming said it was nonsense. She never would learn to have poise and be graceful if she didn't dance. It was never too soon to learn. Besides, she would mix with other children, there, and perhaps grow more like them. Isabella, appealed to, said she liked it very much. That was that. Marjory, sighing, watched Jeanie lay out her best dress. Since she had come home, she had scarcely been allowed to wear any of her new dresses, and never without a pinafore. Jeanie had sniffed and muttered something about fine feathers as she took them out of the trunk, but all the same she made Marjory wear her very best when she went to the dancing class. Isy still had white muslin and a blue sash, but her curls were fatter and more golden than ever. They each carried a bag with a pair of dancing slippers in it, a hair-brush, and a handkerchief. Jeanie carried two white woollen shawls to wrap them in between the dances. They set off on either side of her, wrapped in their cloaks. On the way they stopped next door to call for Isabella Heron, who always accompanied Isy. To-day, however, they were hastily motioned away; Isabella had the measles and was in bed. The maid told Jeanie while the children waited at the gate; they could not hear what she said, but from Jeanie's pursed up face and many nods, they knew it was something gloomy. She told them about it on the way. 'She said she felt all hot and cold the other day, when we were playing,' said Isy, and Jeanie looked sharply at her.

'She did? Well, you're to play with her no more, either of you, and we'll pray the Lord no harm has been done,' she said, anxiously.

The dancing class was held in a big room on the top floor of a near-by school. Outside pupils were accepted just for this class, and you could always tell which they were because they did not cling together in bunches and whisper like the school children did. They went first into an ante-room with bare, white-washed walls with big black pegs. Soon the pegs became filled with cloaks and shawls. There was only one mirror, and most people had to stand on a chair before they could see into it; certainly Marjory did. Several of the other children greeted Isabella, and came sliding over the polished floor to speak to her. They stared at Marjory.

'This is my younger sister,' said Isy rather grandly.

'I've just come from Edinburgh,' said Marjory, but nobody looked at all interested. They turned away without speaking. Jeanie had settled herself on a bench with a large lady in black, who looked rather like Miss Potune, and was deep in conversation. Marjory felt lost. She was very glad when a tall thin lady came out of an inner room, followed by a short fat lady who played the clavecin. The tall lady was Miss McPherson, who took the class. She clapped her hands, and called out 'To your places!' Instantly there was a scurry, as the children slid to and fro across the room. Isy walked up at once, and took her place in the front row. Marjory followed her; she did not want to be separated from the only person she knew. She stood awkwardly behind her, neither in nor out of the row, until Isy turned and saw her.

'You can't stay here, Maidie,' she whispered crossly. 'You'll be in the back row, I expect. Wait till Fersy tells you where to go.'

'I want to stay with you,' said Marjory, her lips trembling.

'Well you can't, then. You're in my place!' said a little girl in bright orange silk, who had come in late. She gave Marjory a sharp push. 'Cry baby!'

Marjory looked desperate. To steady herself, she tried to think of something safe and lovely, of Braehead, and walking by the bridge with Isa. 'Oh, Isa!' she cried in her heart.

Miss McPherson came up to them.

'Now, who's this little girl without a place?' she said, trying to be nice. 'It's little Marjory Fleming! You can't stand next to your sister, dear, because she's with the big girls. Come along. I know you'd like to stand in *this* row, next to little Hamish Grahame.'

'No, I wouldn't,' said Marjory, looking at the floor. 'I want to go home.'

'Home!' cried Miss McPherson, as if she had never heard of it. 'Oh no, my dear, you want to stay and do some lovely dances! Hamish will help you until I have time to come back and show you the way we do it, won't you, Hamish?'

Hamish had carroty hair, and a kilt with much scarlet in it.

'Yes, Miss McPherson,' he said, but when she had gone he put his face close to Marjory and spat at her.

'I want to go home!' he mimicked.

She was appalled. Never had she run to Jeanie with such relief as she did at the end of the class. She hated the dancing. It had drained her of all courage and energy. Yet, at home, when they asked her how she liked it, she whispered 'Quite well, thank you,' and hurried upstairs to write to Isa. Even to her, she only put a fraction of the terror and anger that had seized her.

My dear little Mama,

I was truly happy to hear that you are all well. My mother bid me tell you that you are delaying your visit too long for you will not get out which will be a hard restraint to you. We are surrounded with measles at present on every side for the Herons got it and Isabella Heron was near deaths door and one night her father lifted her out of bed. And she fell down as they thought lifeless. Mr. Heron said that lassie is dead now she said I'm no dead yet she then threw up a big worm nine inches and a half long. My mother regrets that she cannot write to you at present as her eyes are sore. I have begun dancing but am not very fond of it for the boys strikes and mocks me. I have been another night at the dancing and like it better I will write to you as often as I can but I am afraid I shall not be able to write to you every week. I long for you to fold you in my arms I respect you with the respect due to a mother You don't know how I love you so I shall remain your loving child.

M. FLEMING.

Once more terror and guilt rushed upon her, filling her mind with desolation. She was at home, with all her family round her, and she could not be happy. She had left her whole heart behind, with Isa. At night, kneeling for her prayers beside Isy, she felt a pang of remorse and envy. Isy, kneeling in the fire-light with her curls screwed into papers, looked perfectly content. So did William when he clattered downstairs, whistling, on his way to breakfast. So did the baby cramming her spoon into her mouth and making eyes at Jeanie.

They were all pleased and happy with their life. Only Marjory found it insufficient; was dull, cross, and moped in corners.

She began to grow pale and thin, as she always did if her mind
was not settled. Mrs. Fleming was worried, annoyed, and then
worried again. It was ridiculous for a child to carry on like this;
sincerely she wished they had never sent Marjory away. In
vain, softened by the misery in the child's face, she asked
gently:

'What ails you, Maidie? Do you want anything? Tell
Mamma what it is?'

Marjory stared at her in silence. Mamma herself had said . . .
She turned away listlessly.

'I don't know,' she whispered.

She did know. Oh, she knew. But what could anyone do to
help her, unless they sent her off to Braehead by express. Only
for an hour or two in the evening was she like her old self, when
her father came home. She sat up in the storm gable, waiting
for him. As soon as she saw him coming under the arch she ran
downstairs, her eyes shining, her cheeks suddenly pink, to open
the door. She looked like a fairy, springing out of the dark passage in her white dress. He caught her in his arms and carried
her off to the library, where she sat on his knee, her head
against his shoulder, listening while he read to her. Then she
was happy, and her clear laugh rang out. Mr. Fleming, appealed
to, said he saw nothing much amiss with her. Mrs. Fleming
sighed.

At evening, in bed, they kissed her, took away her candle,
and left her alone with her thoughts. Then she faced the things
she pushed out of her mind all day. In October, when the leaves
were falling, there was a big yellow harvest moon. It was light
enough to read by. Isy confessed she learned her lessons by it
when Mamma had gone downstairs. Marjory nodded. She knew
all about the moon. It was quiet time, or unearthly hour between two worlds. Sitting at the end of her bed wrapped in
blankets, she wrote to Isa.

My dear Mother,
You will think that I entirely forget you but I assure you
that you are greatly mistaken. I think of you allways and often

146

sigh to think of the distance between us two loving creatures of
Nature. We have regular hours for all our occupations first at
7 o'clock we go to the dancing and come home at 8 we then
read our bible and get our repeating then we play till 10 then
we get our music till 11 when we get our writing an accounts
we sew from 12 till 1 and play till dinner after which I get my
gramer and then work till five at 7 we come and knit till 8 when
we don't go to the dancing this is an exact description of our
employments You have disappointed us all very much especially me in not coming over every coach I heard I ran to the
window but I was always disappointed I must take a hasty
farewell of her whom I love reverence and doat on and whom I
hope thinks the same of

MARJORY FLEMING.

P.S. An old pack of cards would be very acceptable.

There was no more poetry. She did not begin another journal
at home, and indeed there was very little time. Her day was
much more closely filled than it had been in Edinburgh where,
once lessons were over, she had been free. Only once, in despair
she broke into verse. Isa had gone to Braehead as usual, but
she did not write. Marjory ran downstairs like a mad thing
each time she heard the coach, but it brought nothing for her.
Her heart thumped with pain and distress. Had Isa forgotten
all about her? Perhaps she was glad to have no Marjory to
plague her. She was walking under the trees at Braehead with
Mr. Craigie and the Miss Craufurds, and never thinking about
her small cousin at Kirkcaldy. She tossed her head, and decided
not to care any more; but she cared enough to creep upstairs
and put her longings into verse.

> *Oh Isa why do not you write*
> *I'm out of mind when out of sight*
> *I am afraid your dead and gone*
> *And thus I do begin my moan*
> *O miserable unhappy child*
> *To lose a mistress meek and mild*

With all the graces which adorn
I wish that I was never born
I cannot bear the thought and Oh
Indeed I wish it was not so
Thine eyes with luster will not show
And in the grave where it is drere
Thou shalt be laid a lady fair
It fills my heart with great despair
Indeed I now must say adieu
Both to Isabel and you

She tried not to show her sorrow to anyone, but applied herself carefully to lessons, to playing with Isy, even to the dancing. She stopped saying 'When I was at Edinburgh' and Isa's name scarcely passed her lips. Her mother was pleased; Marjory was getting over her silliness, as she was bound to do in time. She was becoming a much quieter, less awkward, and more tractable child. Strangely enough, it was now that her father began to worry. He, if no-one else, saw that this was not his Marjory; knew that her spirits were quenched. He came upon her once in the garden, alone, her head leaning on her hand, in an attitude of passive weariness that touched him. It was not how a child should be. Still, he knew nothing about little girls; her mother reported her vastly improved. Only once, suddenly, her self-control broke; showed, underneath, the fierce struggle that burned and tore her. William was to go to Braehead, to spend the remaining week of the holidays with his cousins. Mrs. Fleming arranged it; they had not seen him since he was a baby; at thirteen he was a bright, handsome boy, with good manners. She thought her sister would be pleased with him.

Marjory sat up very straight. Her eyes widened, grew darker with emotion. She stammered with longing.

'C-c-can I go too?' she said.

No, certainly not. She was not to be selfish. 'I'm sure poor Isabella has had quite enough of you for a little while, Maidie,' her mother said, reprovingly. 'Let others have their turn.'

'But William doesn't really care,' said Marjory, agonized. 'He can't! He doesn't know Braehead! Please let me go.'

Anyone could tell how much she wanted it. Her whole being quivered. The listening children were silent with pity and embarrassment.

'No, Marjory. Don't let me hear about it again,' said her mother, and added: 'I think it would be nice, if you were to write a little note to your cousin for William to take. It would show her you had not forgotten her great kindness to you.'

Marjory bent her head. It was useless to explain. She suddenly gave it up. 'I'll send her my new music book,' she said, and was surprised at her own voice, so calm and far away; but her mother said:

'You should write, first, to see if Isa will accept it. It is not polite to send gifts like that unless you know it is what your cousin would wish.'

She hurried out of the room, leaving Marjory alone, defiant. She stared out of the window, and sighed. Why did her mother make Isa so remote and untouchable; just by a word, reducing her to the stiff formality of 'your cousin'?

When William drove away in the same coach that had taken her three years ago, he carried the letter in his pocket, carefully sealed. No-one but Isa should have it, and he would be sure to bring a reply. In spite of the careful directions and wrapping the books up into a parcel, it was only a very short letter.

My dear Isa,

I wish I was William that I might see you. I have a musick book for the violincello and harpsichord and a sermon book which I would have sent you if my mother said to ask you first if you would take it

Tell the Miss Craufurds that I always remember them Tell the eldest that I keep the box as a Momento Mori adieu Dear Isa.

P.S. Write the first and last verse of hillvalen again adieu.

She had written it during lesson time, by special permission, and her mother had read it before she sealed it up. Most parents read their children's letters before they were sent; Isy held hers up gladly; only rebellious Marjory stood with her lip stuck out, watching her mother read it through. When the coach had gone she came and kneeled up at the window, her cheek pressed to the cold pane. It was not time for her father to come home. When she moved away, there were tears like rain upon the glass.

Jeanie was in a hurry. They would be late for the dancing. She fussed from room to room, pulling Isy's curls when she combed them out, and pushing things into the bag. Isy, flustered, hurried into her cloak. She dreaded being late and perhaps even missing her place in the front row. So she stood, balanced on her toes in the dark passage, and urged:

'Hurry up, Jeanie! We don't want to be late.'

'It's Miss Maidie we're waiting for,' said Jeanie, puffing heavily; and she called out, 'We'll be on our way downstairs, Miss Maidie.'

Marjory heard her, but she did not answer. She could not hurry this evening. She sat on the floor, shivering. At one minute the room was icy, and the next it was burning hot. Her head banged and ached. When she got to her feet, it was worse. She sank down on the bed, and closed her eyes. The house was all at once very still. Presently she heard footsteps; they stumped angrily upstairs and each one thumped and echoed in her burning head. She tried to sit up, to call out.

'Oh, Isa!' she whispered.

It was not Isa, but Jeanie. The plumes on her bonnet waved grotesquely in the half light. She was in a hurry, because of the dancing. She came close to the bed and her face twisted, grew large, and then faded away again.

'Miss Maidie!' she said, her voice sharp with fear. She bent over her. 'Lord save us, child, you've got a fever.'

'Have I?' said Marjory faintly. She could not help being interested. She had never been ill in her life. She lifted her head to ask more about so momentous a fact, but it was so heavy that she let it fall back on the pillows with a sigh.

'Get Mother,' she said, and closed her eyes.

Marjory was ill. She had the measles.

There was no time after that. Day and night merged into one. There was no light, no sun, but the flickering candle and the fire. Even at high noon, the curtains were drawn, filling the room with a strange, dull glow. People flitted round her bed like shadows. They came and went without reason, hushed, as in a dream. Spoons tinkled on glasses. There was a table at the foot of the bed and it had a great many jugs and bottles and spoons on it. She was always hot, always tired. Sometimes one of the shadows raised her gently, and put a glass to her lips. She murmured 'Isa, Isa.' But it was never Isa. She never heard that light, clear voice answering hers, 'I'm here, Muffy.' Isa never came. Only the shadows flitted and hushed, sponging her face, lifting her. A hundred hands ministered to her, but never the two she wanted most in the world. Only once, feebly, she put out her own and grasped a different pair of hands, strong, loving.

'Father!' she said, half wondering, and opened her eyes.

He smiled at her. He was the same, she saw with relief. Not anxious, hushed, like the shadows were. Faintly, she smiled back.

'I've had a fever,' she said, proudly.

Mother and Jeanie were there, too, now. The shadows had gone. The room came back into perspective. Mother looked tired and pale. She was wrapped in a shawl as if she had not been to bed all night.

'You look sad, Mamma,' said Marjory, and then she added, 'Did Isy miss her dancing?'

They exchanged glances. That was a week ago now. A week of sickness and waking nights lay in between. William had gone back to school. Isy was staying with friends, to be out of infection. Mother patted her pillow.

'Don't worry, dearest,' she said.

Marjory opened her eyes wide. In her white face they gleamed and shone, dark as ebony and strangely bright. Worry! Why should she? How odd people were. She closed them again, suddenly weary.

★ *Part Five* ★

'Does Isa—know I've had a fever?' she asked, faintly, and fell asleep.

She had measles, just like Isabella Heron. The doctor told her so when he came. He was very big and jovial, and he made silly jokes. She thought they were silly. She stared at him with disfavour, looking pinched and pale against the warm crimson shawl in which she was wrapped. He thought he had never seen such a plain, solemn child. Not a smile could he get from her.

'Well, young lady, you're in fashion, you see!' he said as he came in, rubbing his hands. 'Five little ladies like you I've had down with measles, in the last week.'

'I've had a fever,' said Marjory obstinately. It sounded grander like that. All the heroines in the love novels had fever. Measles was nothing.

'Tut, tut,' said Dr. Johnstone. He did not look pleased. He turned to her mother.

'Fifteen in the last week, ma'am, if you'll believe me,' he continued. 'And we thought the epidemic was at an end.'

Mrs. Fleming did believe him. She said it was shocking.

'Just let me look at the tongue,' he went on, turning to Marjory again. She was glad of the opportunity. She stuck it out as far as it would go. Dr. Johnstone said 'Tut, tut.' He made a thorough examination, and looked very wise. He had bled her once when she had been delirious, and did not think it necessary again. He recommended a purge. He did not speak to Marjory, but whispered over his shoulder to Mrs. Fleming, who stood attentively by. At last it was over. He took up his hat.

'Good-bye, little lady!' he said, still jovial. Marjory looked away. She said nothing. Mrs. Fleming showed him out of the room.

Convalescence was slow. Marjory was drained of all strength. She could not even hold a pen to write to Isa, and so she did not write. Her mother, anxious to please, offered to write for her, anything she liked to dictate; but Marjory shook her head. She could not write to Isa until she was well. She *must* get well.

152

It was winter now. The trees were bare, the sky grey and cold. She looked at it, wondering, from the cheerful room. She always had a fire, now, the only toys she cared for were laid on the bed beside her. They were tiny things; a little silver watering-can the size of a charm, a tiny little scent bottle, and a few pottery rabbits with broken ears. She was quite contented. She swallowed, uncomplaining, all Dr. Johnstone's physic. At evening, when the lamps were lit, her father came to read to her. He read whatever she liked, and there was no Isy or William to contradict. She liked poetry; especially, again and again, she begged for 'Helvellyn'. Isa had copied it out in her last letter, and her father, reading it, set free a host of memories to drift over her bed.

> *But meeter for thee, gentle lover of nature,*
> *To lay down thy head like the meek mountain lamb*
> *When wildered he drops from some cliff huge in stature*
> *And draws his last sob by the side of his dam.*
> *And more stately thy couch, by this desert lake lying*
> *Thine obsequies sung by the grey plover flying*
> *With only one friend but to witness thy dying*
> *In the arms of Helvellyn and Catchedicam.*

She was back once more in the schoolroom at Braehead, on a hot summer's day, with all her cousins round her. Her father ceased reading. She sighed, drawn back to the present by the silence of the room.

'It makes death sound so lovely,' she said. 'Cool and peaceful and deep. I should not be afraid of it, if it were like that.'

'You have no need to be afraid of it,' he answered, almost roughly. She did not answer. She lay so still he thought that she was asleep and went softly away.

Presently her mother came in. She glanced anxiously at the small, still figure on the bed, and knelt down by the fire. Gently, not to make a noise, she stirred the logs to flame. In sickness, her child was her own again. Marjory had clung to her, whispering 'Mother'. She did not know that she called Isabella her mother too. She knelt, watching the little flames leap up. She had not always understood Marjory. She saw that now. Such a strange, wayward, obstinate little creature; so childlike and so unchildish. She smiled, thinking of it. She was drawn from her reverie by a light voice from the bed.

'Mother,' it said, softly.

She came over to the bed hastily.

'It's only me, making up the fire, my love,' she said anxiously. 'Just go off to sleep again, like a good girl.'

Marjory was wide awake. She stared at the ceiling.

'When I am well again,' she said, 'do you think Isa will come? I cannot give her the measles now.'

Mrs. Fleming sighed. She went back to the fire.

'We'll see,' she said. She did not sound pleased. Marjory noticed it. Lying in bed made you different. Instead of feeling hurt, she felt sorry.

'Mother,' she said again, unexpectedly. 'I do love you so very much.'

'Come, come, Maidie. You get too excited,' was all her mother said, but she sounded pleased all the same. Laying down the fire-irons she came back to the bed.

'Can I get you anything, my love?'

Marjory sighed, she tried to think of something.

'No thank you,' she said at last. 'Only if you would just leave the room door open a wee bit and play "The Land o' the Leal" and I will lie and think and enjoy myself.'

Her mother went downstairs. The child lay still. Between the light sound of the music, and the drifting shadows, she felt at peace. The shadows moved over the ceiling like the branches of a tree; the great trees at Braehead. . . . The music too, sounded like water. Where was Isa now?

Marjory was better. At last she was to come downstairs and spend the afternoon on the settee beside the fire. Her father carried her down, so wrapped in quilts and shawls she resembled a chrysalis. Jeanie and Mrs. Fleming came behind, carrying more shawls. They laid her carefully on the sofa, with her books and toys.

'Tell us if there is anything you want, my love,' they said, eager to please. Everyone was eager to please her these days. She leaned back wearily on the cold, unfamiliar parlour cushions.

'I'd like Isy to come,' she said.

Isabella had come home as soon as the fear of infection was over. William had gone back to school. She came in, calm, and neat as usual, her curls brushed, her dress smooth. She never came into a room tempestuously, as Marjory did. She brought a stool close to the settee and sat on it carefully, arranging her dress.

'Would you like to play something?' she asked. 'Or shall I read to you?'

There it was again! They all tried to please her, to do what she wished, when she only yearned that they should be the same. A little cold fear crept into her heart. It curled there as if it knew its place: it had come to her before, at Ravelston, and beside her darling burn; even beautiful Braehead had not been strong enough to drive it away. Only then she had shrunk from it, bewildered and afraid. Now she looked it in the face, bravely, learned all there was to know, and peace came. She folded her hands on the coverlet, and her eyes lightened suddenly. She lay in her weakened child's body, and she was no longer a child.

'Do you remember our walks in Raith?' she said to Isabella, who looked at her with wide blue eyes.

'We'll go there again, as soon as you are strong enough,' she answered, and Marjory said with a smile: Yes, you must. I should like you to.'

Mrs. Fleming brought her sewing and sat with them. She looked contented. Isabella leaned against her, because the stool had no back. Marjory lay still, watching them. They seemed very close to her, and yet immeasurably distant. She thought of Isa. Oh, if her thought could pierce the walls, fly over the sea, and find her. She would know what Marjory knew. She would look at her once with her wise, laughing eyes and say, 'So that's it! Well, be good, Muffy, until I come for you.' But her mother was happy, because Marjory was better.

155

★ Part Five ★

It was only a question of time now, the doctor said. Isabella laughed and talked of what they would do as soon as Marjory could go out. She had to lie still, playing at being a child again, while inside her, her spirit fluttered, newly born, pressing against the walls that held it.

She smiled.

'You're not tired, Marjory?' said her mother anxiously, throughout the afternoon. She shook her head. She laughed. She became very gay; quite herself again. She took her physic without a murmur, and said she was sure it had done her good. A little colour crept into her cheeks, deepened by the glow from the fire as the light faded. Evening came. The lamps were lit.

'Good-bye, day!' said Marjory, looking out at the wintry garden before the curtains were drawn. Her eyes wandered, anxiously, to the door, with love.

'Is Father coming?' she asked, a hundred times. Mrs. Fleming glanced at the clock; he would not be long now.

In another minute the front door slammed. He came at once to the sofa, and kissed her; he had eyes for no-one else. She slipped her arms round his neck.

'Tired, Maidie?'

'No, Father. Not at all.'

He patted her shoulder.

'That's a good girl. I'll soon have you running to meet me again, eh?'

She did not answer. She pressed her forehead against his shoulder, and whispered: 'Lift me up! I'm tired of sitting still.'

In an instant he had swung her up into his arms, quilt and all. She lay passive, her head against his shoulder as he walked up and down the room. She was as light as a feather. Holding her, he felt with alarm how thin and light she had grown. Only her eyes seemed to be larger and darker; they shone very brightly in the firelight. Presently she said:

'Father, I will repeat something to you; what would you like?'

He smiled down at her, amused at her earnest voice. She gazed back, unsmiling. It was her only chance to tell them, now, when she lay safe and sheltered in his arms. She waited.

'Just choose yourself, Maidie,' he said at last.

She hesitated, and then clearly, brilliantly, she gave them her message. He stopped walking, holding her tightly. Her eyes shone, deepened, flickered with tears.

> *Why am I loth to leave this earthly scene?*
> *Have I so found it full of pleasing charms?*
> *Some drops of joy, with draughts of ill between*
> *Some gleams of sunshine 'mid renewing storms,*
> *Is it departing pangs my soul alarms?*
> *Or Death's unlovely, dreary, dark abode?*
> *For guilt, for guilt my terrors are in arms,*
> *I tremble to approach an angry God,*
> *And justly smart beneath his sin-avenging rod.*

> *Fain would I say, forget my foul offence,*
> *Fain promise nevermore to disobey:*
> *But should my Author health again dispense*
> *Again I might forsake fair Virtue's way,*
> *Again in folly's path might go astray,*
> *Again exalt the brute, and sink the man.*
> *Then how should I for heavenly mercy pray*
> *Who act so counter heavenly mercy's plan*
> *Who sin so oft have mourned, yet to temptation ran?*

The lines were from Burns, but it was all Marjory. She called, across the sea, to Isa for forgiveness.

There was silence. She stared, hurt, at her father's face, twisted and unreal. He turned away, but the arms that held her shook. He laid her gently back on the sofa next to Isy, round-eyed and wondering.

'Please give me my slate, Mamma,' she begged. 'I want to write a poem.'

Mrs. Fleming looked startled.

'Oh, Marjory—your eyes,' she began doubtfully, but her father said roughly: 'Let her have it.' He looked at her for a minute, in silence.

The slate was brought. Though her fingers could hardly press on the chalk, she quickly wrote a poem of fourteen lines 'To her loved cousin on the Author's recovery'. It would go where neither her voice, nor her most loving thoughts could carry.

Oh Isa pain did visit me
I was at the last extremity
How often did I think of you
I wished your graceful form to view
To clasp you in my weak embrace
Indeed I thought I'd run my race
Good care I'm sure was of me taken
But still indeed I was much shaken
At last I daily strength did gain
And oh! at last away went pain
At length the doctor thought I might
Stay in the parlour till the night
I now continue so to do
Farewell to Nancy and to you.

Wrote by M.F.

She laid down her pencil with a sigh.
'I think I am a little tired,' she said, and was still.

Next day she was ill. She woke in the night, sobbing, for the pain in her head. Candles were lit, doors flew open, they came running; but it was no longer any good. Her mother pressed cold cloths to her head, and they burned like fire. She lay, tossing and turning, the tears running down her cheeks.

'My head, my head,' she told them over and over again, her eyes beseeching; it was all she could say.

The doctor came at daylight. He burst into the darkened room like the sun, still jovial and quite untouched. Hope revived; Mrs. Fleming hung on to his every word. Only the patient lay still, her dark eyes open, unmoved. They looked straight into his eyes, and for one minute a smile flickered, and was gone. He did not rub his hands; the joke faded away, unuttered. He made his examination in silence, and then turned to her mother.

'A word in private with you, ma'am,' he said, bowing, and looking wiser than ever. Once more, he glanced at the child in the bed. Propped up by a mountain of pillows, she stared back. You could not tell what she was thinking. Her panic of the night was over; the pain momentarily subdued. She had a kind of dignity—it was nonsense, of course. Children were amusing little creatures, to be petted or teased. He made one more effort to win her favour, half surprised at his eagerness to do so.

'She'll do very well—very well indeed,' he said, nodding his head. 'We will soon get over this little attack. In the meantime here's a little reward for your patience, Miss Marjory.'

He put down a silver sixpence on the coverlet close to her hand. She took it up. He had half expected her to toss it back at him, but she thanked him. She turned it over and over and a little colour came into her cheeks.

'Will you let me out at the New Year?' she asked eagerly, looking up at him.

He smiled down at her genially. It was December the 16th.

'Well, and why are you so anxious to be let out then? Come; it's only fair to give me your reason!'

She was silent.

'Tell the doctor, Maidie,' persuaded her mother.

Marjory looked up, struggling for words. Leaning forward she at last managed to say:

'I want to buy a present for my dear Isa Keith with the sixpence you gave me, and should like to choose it myself!'

Then she lay back on her pillows, and was silent.

It had only been a brief interlude. The pain returned again and again. Three days she lay in her darkened room, half conscious, while the shadows flitted about the bed. She could not speak, except to sob for the pain. Perhaps she could not think. Perhaps, the shadowy trees at Braehead stretched down from the ceiling to meet her, and Isa walked beneath them in her cool white dress.

The morning came, pale and unreal, pressing against the

window. It was Thursday, December the 19th. The room was still. The embers of last night's fire gleamed in the grate. All the thoughts, the hopes of the living were turned to the bed. She lay still, neither awake nor asleep. Then, at last, she opened her eyes wide. Looking beyond the room and her mother's outstretched hand, to whom did she call 'Mother, Mother'? She died, aged eight years and eleven months, and was buried at Kirkcaldy.

Her father never mentioned her name again.

London,
   September–December 1944.

Appendix A

<hr>

THE LIFE OF MARY QUEEN OF SCOTS BY M.F.

Poor Mary Queen of Scots was born
With all the graces which adorn
Her birthday is so very late
That I do now forget the date
Her education was in france [*sic*]
There she did learn to sing and dance
There she was married to the dauphin
But soon he was laid in a coffin
Then she at once from France retired
Where she had been so much admired
Farewell dear france she cried at last
While a despairing look she cast
The nobels came to meet there Queen
Whom they before had never seen
They never saw a face so fair
For there is no such beauties there
That with her they could compair
She was a Roman Catholic strong
Nor did she think that it was wrong
But they her faith could not well bear
And to upbraid her they would dare
There was a man that was quite good
To preach against her faith he would
His name was John Knox a reformer
Of Mary he was a great scorner
Her nation was so very fierce
That they your very hart could pierce

In love she fell and deep it was
Lord Darnly was the very cause
A nobels son a handsome lad
By some queer way or other had
Got quite the better of her hart
With him she always talked apart
Silly he was but very fair
A greater buck was not found there
He was quite tall and slender too
And he could dance as well as you
Soon was the nupsials done and ore
Of it there was said nothing more
They lived together for a while
And happiness did there time beguile
Mary was charmed with a player
Of whom she took great great care
He fed upon the finest fair
He was her greatest favourite
Him she caresed with all her might
She gave him food she gave him wine
When he was gone she would repine
The King heard this with anger sore
This is not all there is much more
For he did murder the poor player
Of whom she took so great a care
In agony she heaved a sigh
For on the King she did relie
Bad hatered at length found a way
It was a little more than play
An awful day at last arrived
Which was the last that he survived
For she went to a masqurade
But for that thing he dearly paid
For in her absence what was done
The thing would not I'm sure give fun
The house in which the King did lie
I cannot think without a sigh

Was blowen up at too next day
The King was killed I'm sorry to say
Some degree of suspicion fell
On the mighty Earl of Bothwell
And of the Queen they did think too
That of that thing she quite well knew
For they do think that mary was
Of Darnlys death the very cause
But he was guiltless of the crime
But it was only for that time
Mary went to meet her son
That thing did not give her much fun
For Bothwell under some pretence
And with a great deal of expence
Marched to a town there found the Queen
He was quite glad when she was seen
He then disperced her slender train
That did not give her any pain
His castle of Dunbar she went
It was just there that she was sent
Poor Mary did not shew much terror
I must say this is an great error
This opportunity they catched
For there they did wish to be mached
To Edinburgh the Queen was brought
He was quite glad that she was caught
The castle was then in his power
His temper was quite bad and sowr
There was she lodged in the castle
Which was as bad near as the bastile
He was then married to the Queen
Of whom he did not care a pin
The nobles formed a conspiracy
On poor Bothwell and poor Mary
Kirkcaldy of grange and some more
His name I did not tell before
The nobles soldiars were quite brave

And they there masters lives would save
Poor Bothwells friends were not the same
And spread but small degree of faim
For their poor master they forsook
But in their base flight he pertook
For he said to the Queen, adieu
Those that behave so are but few
The King said to the Queen farewell
For his poor soldiars nearly fell
After Bothwell went away
In a humour not like play
She gave herselfe up with much ease
And she did try them all to please
The soldiars behaved very bad
It would indeed have put me mad
For when she turned her eyes so (bright) (?)
She always saw a dreadful sigh(t)
Darnlys Picture with her poor son
That did not give her any fun
Judge and revenge my cause cried he
This mary could not bear to see
Covered with dust droping a tear
A spectical she did appear
To break her marriage she would not
Though it would happy make her lot
This her bad nobles would not bear
Though she was then so very fair
To Lochlevin was she then carried
She would not say she was not married
At last from prison she got away
She got from prison I do say
All her great arts she had employed
And the success she had enjoyed
Her keepers brother gained she had
He was a very fine young lad
At last she hinted that she would
Make him her husband if she could

On Sunday night the second of may
She did escape that very day
At supper when his brother sat
I have not got a rhyme for that
And all the family had retired
His cleverness I much admired
One of this friends stole of the keys
To let her out when she did please
Let out poor Mary and her maid
Indeed she got from him much aid
But for that thing his brother paid
She got to the boat which was prepaired
Nobody but george for her cared
There she did meet her friends on shore
Who had been there some time before
At Setons house she sat some time
There she got good bread and good wine
She then got up and rode away
Full of great mirth and full of play
To Hamilton (?) she came at last
For she did galop very fast
Then she her followeres all prepaired
And fealty to their Queen they sweared
They marched against the regent who
Could perhaps fight as wel as you
Mary meanwhile was on a hill
Where she did stand up quite stock still
The regent Murry ganed them all
And every one of hers did fall
She then did mount again to ride
For in her friends she couldnt confide
She flew to England for protection
For Elisabeth was her connection
Elisbeth was quite cross and sour
She wished poor Mary in her power
Elisbeth said she would her keep
And in her kingdon she might sleep

But to a prison she was sent
Elisbeths hart did not relent
Full nineteen years and mayhap more
Her legs became quite stiff and sore
At last she heard she was to die
And that her soul would mount the sky
She was quite overjoyed at this
She thought it was her greatest bliss
The hour of death at last drew nigh
Then she did mount the scaffold high
Upon the block she laid her head
She was as calm as if in bed
One of the men her head did hold
And then her head was of I'm told
There ends all Queen Elisbeths foes
And those who at her bend their bows
Elisbeth was a cross old maid
Now when her youth began to fade
Her temper was worce then before
And people did not her adore
But Mary was much loved by all
Both by the great and by the small
But hark her soul to heaven did rise
And I do think she gained a prise
For I do think she would not go
Into the awfull place below
There is a thing that I must tell
Elisbeth went to fire and hell
Him who will teach her to be cevel
It must be her great friend the divel.

Appendix B

EXTRACTS FROM LETTERS TO AND CONCERNING HER, ETC.

LETTER A

(Isabella Keith to Isabella Fleming: 1 April 1811. Fragmentary. *On the back* of Marjory's letter which alone contains the date 'Edinburgh, 1 April 1811' and begins 'My dear Isabella I hear that your health . . .')

My Dear Isabella,

I hope you will excuse the shortness of Maidie's letter and trusting to a longer one from her soon accept of a few lines from me instead,—she is going on very busily with her lessons in all of which she is I hope improving, except her musick she dislikes it so much that she loses all patience, but I hope when she gets the length of playing a Tune she will like it better and pay more attention. She is very fond of History and is reading the history of Scotland at present in which she is much interested. She continues her journal every day entirely by herself it is a very amusing production indeed, and when finished I shall send it over for your Mothers perusal, and I hope she will find it more correct and better written than the last. I have almost entirely given up her dancing, as it took up a great deal too much time, and a few lessons a year or two after this will do her infinitely more good, she is grown excessively fat and strong, but I cannot say she is a great beauty just now, as she has lost her two front teeth, and her continual propensity to laugh exhibits the defect rather unbecomingly. I have now I think said enough of our dear Muffy, and will talk of other matters. The next great object of our interest is the dear ...

LETTER B.

(The same to Marjory Fleming: October or November 1811)

My dear Marjory,

I take the opportunity of your brother Williams going over to write you a few lines, which I hope you will not delay answering. I cannot see that a letter once a week can be a great hardship to you as it might serve instead of your writing Lesson, and you will always find plenty to say if you tell me about your Mother your Sisters and Yourself:

I am still enjoying this delightful weather at sweet Braehead. Margaret has been rather delicate for a few weeks past, and is not able to take long walks, but Isabella and I go to Barnbougle and the Seaside every day, I very often take my little glass and look over to Kirkaldie, I see Raith Tower perfectly plainly, and I would see Kirkaldie too were it not situated in the bay. This would be very pleasant, for with a telescope I could distinguish the figures on the opposite side of the water and then I might perhaps see you and Isa at play in the fields, only I am afraid I might sometimes be vexed by observing your behaviour to gentle Isa which I am sorry to hear is not exactly what it ought to be do you remember what conversations you and I used to have on this subject?—and how when you were young, and that you were resolved you should always for the future be kind and obedient to her. I hope in your next Letter you will be able to tell me you are trying to be mild and tractable and good humoured.

I long much my dear daughter to see you and talk over all our old stories together, and to hear you read and repeat. I am tiring for my old friend Cesario, and for poor Lear, and wicked Richard: how is the dear Multiplication Table going on,—are you still as much attached to 9 times 9 as you used to be?

I have not Helvellyn here, but I think I can remember it by heart pretty correctly:

I climbed the dark brow of the mighty Helvellyn
Lakes and Mountains around me gleamed misty and wide
All was still save by fits the wild Eagle was yelling
And starting around me the Echos replied
On the right Striden Edge round the Red Tarn was bending
And Catchedicam its left verge was defending
One huge nameless rock in the midst was ascending
When I marked the sad spot where the wanderer had died.

Dark green was that spot midst the brown Mountain heather
Where the pilgrim of nature lay stretched in decay
Like the corpse of an outcast abandoned to weather
While the mountain winds wasted the tenantless clay
Yet not quite deserted though lonely extended
For faithful in death one mute favorite attended
The much loved remains of his Master defended
And chased the hill fox and the Raven away.

(and so on, twenty-four more lines, ending with the lines
Marjory was always quoting):

But meeter for thee gentle Lover of Nature
        (To bow) down thy head like the meek Mountain Lamb
When wildered it drops from some cliff huge in sta(ture)
And draws its last sob by the side of its Dam
And more stately thy couch by this desert Lake ly(ing)
Thy obsequies sung by the gray plover flying
With one only friend but to witness thy dying
In the arms of Helvellyn and Catchedicam.

May and Isy Crawfurd send their love and a Kiss to you. I
wish I had you by me, and I would give you twenty myself
farewell my dear Muff dont forget your Isabella.

I am very much pleased with William's manner, and so were
all here, I regret I saw so little of him, but he has promised to
write to me,—

I opened my letter again to say how much I am obliged to
you for the off(er of the) Sermons and the Music book. If it is

not robbing your Mother or yourself I (would) receive them with great gratitude, and would feel their value encreased in (———) were you to exercise your wits in writing a line or two of poetry in the (———) page of each:—

(*Addressed*):   For

                Miss Muff, Maidie, Marjory Fleming

                Kirkaldy

                favored by *Rare* Rear Admiral Fleming.

                i.e., William.

LETTER C

(Mrs. Fleming to Isabella Keith: 9 January 1812)

. . . Her poor Father unceasingly deplores his loss, I fear he idolised her too much and was too vain of her talents. . . .

To tell you what your poor Maidie said of you would fill volumes, for you was the constant theme of her discourse, the subject of her thoughts, and ruler of her actions—for what would reflect credit or reproach on your tuition were the motives by which she was chiefly actuated or restrained, and I loved her the more for the affection she bore you, which was truly filial. The last time she mentioned you was a few hours before all sense save that of suffering was suspended when she said to Dr. Johnstone 'If you will let me out at the New Year I will be quite contented'. I asked what made her so anxious to get out then; she replied 'I wish to purchase a new years gift for Isa: Keith with the Sixpence you gave me for being patient during the Measels, and would like to chuse it myself.' I do not recollect her speaking afterwards except to complain of her poor head, till just before she expired when she articulated oh Mother Mother. I send with this what she esteemed most her Bibles for you and pocket book for Nancy . . . (and hair. . . Asks for a portrait of Maidie and copies of Burns' 'Why am I loath' and the speech of Constance 'Look who comes here'.)

LETTER D

(Isabella Keith to Mrs. Fleming, in answer to the above: after 15 Jan. 1812)

I have all her writing copies, spelling book, and many other little trifles which I collected after she left me, any of which or even her journals, much as I value all of them, if you wish for them I shall part with but only to her Mother will I ever relinquish the smallest trifle that ever belonged to her. . . .

. . . the strictness and severity of the mistress which I have often found a painful restraint on my affection. I should have enjoyed her society as a companion and a playmate; it is foolish and needless to harass myself with such regrets. . . .

I am sorry to see from what he (Mr. Fleming) says, that he anticipates success in my attempt to trace our dear childs features, the sketch I have is a few coarse lines, in which I believe nobody but myself could trace any resemblance, as I never have been in the habit of drawing any finished picture of that kind, the little sketch I shall make, will be of the slightest nature, such as it shall turn out, you shall have it, but I fear my own over anxiety to produce a likeness will, (as I have often found the case) be fatal to my success in the attempt. . . .

Note: Isabella Keith married the brother of Christopher North, and had two children. She died in 1837.